D1616556

March 2022/ Vol. 50, No. 1

Publisher

Dr. Ida Rolf Institute®
5055 Chaparral Ct., Ste. 103
Boulder, CO 80301 USA
(303) 449-5903
(303) 449-5978 Fax
(800) 530-8875

Structure, Function, Integration: Journal of the Dr. Rolf Institute (ISBN: 978-1-7332838-7-8, ISSN 1538-3784) is published by Dr. Ida Rolf Institute 5055 Chaparral Ct., Ste. 103 Boulder, CO 80301 USA.

Original Art by
Orange Identity

March Cover Art

Enlightening the Axial Complex

Inspired by Jan H. Sultan and his thoughts about how to see and work with the axial complex, this cover art is the concept of Editor-in-Chief Lina Amy Hack and the design team of Orange Identity. Rolfers® and Rolf Movement® practitioners have different 'lenses' through which they view the anatomy of their clients. The axial complex is considered a regional study, especially how its anatomy is functionally presented during a session's body reading. This cover overlays a few of these ideas. When Rolfers ask themselves, "What is happening in the axial complex of this client?" they are tailoring their viewing to the head, spine, and sacrum with a broad consideration for all the connecting structures from there. One must contemplate the contents of this region: the brain, the spinal cord, the fluidic neurons destined for peripheral function. All this circuitry is embedded in tracks and sheets of fascia. We may talk about the bones – the skull, the vertebrae, and the sacrum - but we imply that these places are landmarks for the territory of interest. Ida P. Rolf, PhD, gave us the idea that 'gravity is the therapist', and gravity is pulling on the internal waters of the body.

Contents

From the Editor-in-Chief

Lina Amy Hack

"The appearance of this quarterly seems a promise that Structural Integration has finally come of age. As such it is indeed a joyous occasion for me personally, calling for celebration and good wishes. I can imagine nothing more festive and appropriate for this milestone than this medium of communication as projected by our editors. It will continue to be a source of inspiration to me that we can talk among ourselves of the things that interest us, and that we can collect and record, as well as exchange, thoughts that relate to us and our field."

– Ida P. Rolf, PhD, from the *Bulletin of Structural Integration* (1968), Volume 1, Number 1.

With this issue of *Structure, Function, Integration (SFI): The Journal of the Dr. Ida Rolf Institute®* (DIRI), we are celebrating another milestone. This is the 50th volume of what was initially the *Bulletin of Structural Integration* and I also feel inspired by this medium of communication. This is my first issue as Editor-in-Chief of SFI, after two years of mentoring and co-leadership with Anne Hoff. I feel a great depth of gratitude to her for this training.

Allow me to take a moment and reflect on Anne's monumental stewardship of our journal. She started as a volunteer editor in the year 2000. In those early years, she was part of the editorial team led by Stephen Paré that updated *Rolf Lines: The Journal of The Rolf Institute®* to *Structural Integration: The Journal of The Rolf Institute*. Paré helmed the shift from a newsletter with foundational articles to a higher-quality journal, regularly featuring significant authors in our profession. With the December 2006 issue of *Structural Integration*, Anne became Editor-in-Chief. In her sixteen-year tenure, she curated regular columns, featured a wide variety of themes, and held the vision of how important the printed word is for our profession. She oversaw another transition where, in 2018, our journal became *SFI* and took another leap forward with design enhancements and platforming for broader distribution through Amazon. As Anne passes the baton to me, I feel so much admiration for her work and for the team of editors who are the heart of this publication; there is a momentum that I have stepped into, and I intend to further the mission of this journal as a place where we can "talk among ourselves of the things that interest us," and continue to "collect and record" our good ideas – for Rolfers®, for the broader structural integration (SI) community, for allied professionals, and for an interested public.. This is the living legacy of Dr. Rolf's teachings, found in these pages, from 1968 to now, and the dynamic conversations taking place in our profession.

A few details may have struck you when reading the above quote; our DIRI journal has been at times a quarterly published four times a year; in the 1980s, they were monthly for a time; in the 2010s, it was two times a year, and we have landed on three publications in 2022. Also, if you have already done the math from that 1968 quote, you'll already have realized that 2022 marks fifty-four years since that first issue. Let me tell you that I have been studying the past publications, and even though volume 1, number 1, has on the cover the date 1968 (see Figure), the catalog of the journal records it as the first issue of 1969. So, volume 1 is winter 1969, according to our formal records. Throughout the 1970s, the volume number did not change each year as it does now. Also, it appears that no issues were printed in 1978, and volume numbers were not marked in many issues of *Rolf Lines* in the 1980s. In 1991, the editors of *Rolf Lines* updated that year's volume number to the 19th volume, after that, increased by one each new year. Leading us here, 2022 being our 50th volume.

For this first issue of 2022, our golden anniversary, we offer you the theme of the axial complex, starting with a poem and then several viewpoints from our Rolfing® SI and Rolf Movement® faculty, as well as articles by other valued instructors. Our columns feature the popular Letter from the Embryo by Konrad Obermeier.

This month's Fascia Insights interviews Dr. Thomas Rosenkilde Rasmussen, lead researcher of a 2021 peer-reviewed publication about the direct measurement of the cranium's third rhythm. Our Perspectives section has a diverse collection of article topics. The first two articles elaborate on presentations from the 2016 Fascia Research Summer School held in Leipzig, Germany. Those are followed by an article with some helpful notes about inflammation. We have an interview with newly minted Advanced Rolfing Instructor Pierpaola Volpones. Lastly, Anne Hoff offers a thoughtful discussion about "Cultural Humility in the Therapeutic Relationship." All this, plus our book reviews, is a brief invitation to dive into the pool's deep end with us, the authors, and our journal editors. Please do reach out with your thoughts (linabehie@hotmail.com), and be prepared to be asked to write them for these pages. Let's hold our debate here, on these pages, with well-reasoned and thought-provoking ideas.

Sincerely,
Lina Amy Hack

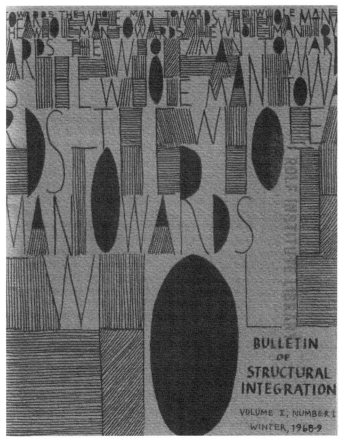

Cover of the first journal, *Bulletin of Structural Integration*, of the then Rolf Institute®.

Fascia Insights

Third Rhythm of the Cranium

By Lina Amy Hack, Certified Advanced Rolfer®, and Thomas
Rosenkilde Rasmussen, PhD, MSC, CST-D

ABSTRACT *For years the primary evidence of the third rhythm of the cranium
was observation by palpation. In 2021 Dr. Thomas Rosenkilde Rasmussen and Dr.
Karl Christian Meulengracht published their results of direct observation of the third
rhythm using robotics and software analysis in their peer-reviewed publication, "Direct
measurement of the rhythmic motions of the human head identifies a third rhythm"
in the* Journal of Bodywork and Movement Therapies. *In this interview, Rasmussen
discusses his background as medical researcher and craniosacral practitioner that led
to building this measurement machine, doing this experiment, and the various questions
his laboratory group are considering for the future.*

Lina Amy Hack

Thomas Rosenkilde Rasmussen

Lina Amy Hack: Thank you for meeting
with me, where do I find you today for this
interview?

Thomas Rosenkilde Rasmussen: I'm in
Copenhagen, Denmark. And where are
you now?

LAH: Ah, Saskatoon, Saskatchewan,
Canada. Great to connect at such great
distances.

Today we're going to talk about your
2021 peer-reviewed publication, "Direct
measurement of the rhythmic motions of
the human head identifies a third rhythm,"
which was published in the *Journal of
Bodywork and Movement Therapies*
(Rasmussen and Meulengracht 2021).

Can you tell me a little bit about your
background, are you a researcher and a
practitioner?

TRR: My background is, I have a PhD in
medicine and I worked for fifteen years
as a scientist in cancer research. I was
a research leader for many years. And
then, at one point I became an associate
professor at a young age. I was thinking,
what do I want to do now? And I decided
that I really want to learn about manual
therapy. Every time I asked questions
about it, it was clear, we don't have
the same kind of research in the field
of manual therapy as you have in
cancer research.

As a profession, manual therapists had become stuck in a logical circle, because everyone is quoting everyone else saying the same thing when they define the rate of the cranial rhythm. But where does this come from?

Then I spent some time learning craniosacral therapy from Upledger Institute International, then visceral manipulation and neural manipulation from the Barral Institute. Then I sent myself to osteopathic school in Europe and stepped back from my hard science work for some years, because I wanted to learn by hand and by experience. Coming into some of the topics, it was a fight between my left and right brain, because at one point I was a very experimental scientist, and here in manual therapy, people were just discussing their experiences. Especially the experiences people had with fascia. How can fascia react the way that fascia reacts? And it's not controlled alone, in our view, by the central nervous system. I got triggered by that, as a lot of people didn't know [the important details involved]. My inquiry became focused on the cranial rhythm – when I put my hands on the cranium – do I feel a rhythm because I imagine it? Because it is so gentle, I was really caught in my own head about this.

At one point, I ended up in many left-brain discussions about it. I studied further with Upledger Institute International, then I became a teacher of craniosacral therapy, I taught a lot of classes and students frequently questioned the existence of a rhythm different from the respiratory and cardiac rhythms. We could only find one real study that was very clear about measuring the cranial movement by Viola Frymann, DO, FAAO (1921-2016). Back in the seventies, she built a machine to measure the rhythmic motions of the cranium *in situ* (Frymann 1971).

With modern technology, we built a machine with sensors that could detect down to one micrometer of movement. So now we have a validated machine.

All of us doing craniosacral therapy, we all had this view about what the craniosacral rhythm was, what we had been reading in the textbooks. And then we began to find out that a lot of it is actually not true. The third rhythm, it doesn't change. It's a very fundamental rhythm. And then, this was the beginning.

We had to say, okay, we need to go back and do a very basic study to do very basic measurements. We had to stop thinking of the textbooks we have all read about the craniosacral rhythm. As a profession, manual therapists had become stuck in a logical circle, because everyone is quoting everyone else saying the same thing when they define the rate of the cranial rhythm. But where does this come from?

We measured hundreds of people just to learn. And also, to become aware of all the variables that move the cranium in the micrometer range. Now we have the clear knowledge that when you breathe, that will make your skull move. People say the skull can't move. Now we know, the head is moving when we breathe, we measured it. And we could measure the arterial rhythm in the head (see Figure 1). Then we asked ourselves, how do we make a very clear distinguishing measurement between the different rhythms that move the cranium internally? To answer this, we did Fourier transformations to separate all the different rhythms of the skull from the raw data. This is the technology we have now. And it became a much longer project than we expected. We had to start at the beginning, looking at the data, we just called it a third rhythm to make clear the fact that the skull has a movement that is not respiratory breathing, and it is not the heartbeat.

We needed to define that first. In this study, we invited fifty people to be our participants. We made sure that the people didn't know what craniosacral therapy was, many of them had never heard about it. And there was no therapist

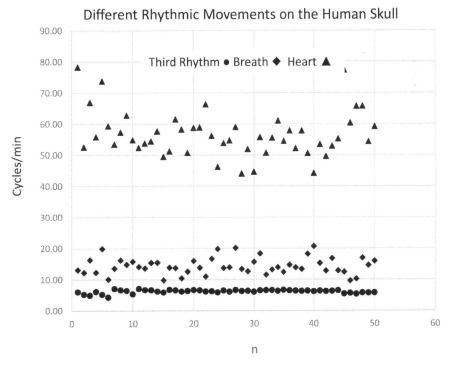

Figure 1: The three different rhythmic movements of the human skull, the average of each participant is reported by a data point, along the x-axis, n indicating participant number, and the y-axis is the cycles per minute of the movement observed. For each participant a circle indicates the average of their identified third rhythm, a diamond indicates their average respiratory rhythm, and a triangle indicates their average heart rate. Creative Commons license: CC BY-NC-ND 4.0.

The sensors we had on the participants' heads are called servo actuators and you can program the amount of pressure they apply to the head. Even when the head was expanding, normally a machine would have an increase in pressure and the head would meet resistance, but here the machine is programmed to keep the same pressure on the participant's skin, no matter where it moves.

in the room. We programmed the machine to observe the participant lying supine, on their own.

LAH: That is what struck me about your paper, in the body of knowledge of manual therapy, your 2021 article fills an important gap. You have begun to characterize the normal behavior of the third cranial rhythm that we believe to be the product of cerebrospinal fluid production and absorption in the central nervous system. This is a foundational piece and for my colleagues, structural integration practitioners specifically, we need this knowledge about what is actually happening in the skull.

Let's define a few terms for our readers, in your paper you write about the primary respiratory mechanism and the cranial rhythmic impulse. What are these two terms and how are they different?

TRR: We can say that the primary respiratory mechanism was a concept made by William Sutherland, DO, (1873-1954) to define that there is a movement within the head different from the breathing of the lungs which also moves the head (1939). Sutherland never wrote anything about the rate of the rhythm. And in some of Sutherland's texts, there are many different rhythms discussed, some are described more like tides.

The cranial rhythmic impulse, sometimes called cranial rhythmic index, is central to craniosacral evaluation and is a manifestation of the primary respiratory mechanism that is in our body. Cranial rhythmic index became the term used in scientific papers because the primary respiratory mechanism is not clearly defined.

Also, if you look in textbooks and different schools of craniosacral studies, they focus on different rhythms of Sutherland's concept, like the mid-tide, long-tide, and breath of life. These are not clearly defined and they were not defined by Sutherland. So we can say that the Upledger craniosacral school and the other schools of craniosacral therapy, they call the cranial rhythm experienced by palpation the craniosacral rhythm or cranial rhythmic index often showing different range of rates. And we don't know if that was what Sutherland experienced, because what Sutherland experienced, we cannot put hands on and say, "I have the same experience as Sutherland," we just don't know that. In the paper we define a third rhythm experimentally, creating the foundation for further understanding and evidence of the cranial movements used in manual therapy for years.

We asked, what head movements exist when a person is at rest and can we relate them to that palpatory experience that people have?

LAH: Yes, that is a brilliant question. You mentioned Dr. Frymann, she did some measurements of internal head movements in the 1960s and 1970s, but her methodology wasn't conclusive and it is critiqued often. Why didn't that work? What was the weakness of that methodology?

TRR: Number one, it was the software because Frymann's measuring tool needed a very strong physical contact on the head. That pressure alone interfered with the normal movement of the head and it also often created a headache in the people lying down.

LAH: Oh wow, that sounds intense.

TRR: And the second issue was that there were different kinds of movements acting on the head and her methodology couldn't separate them. They would have people hold their breath for a long time. In that Frymann study, there was one client that I think was conclusive. That was a man who was really proficient in holding his breath for a long time. And while he was doing that and not having a headache, you can actually see that there was a movement around seven to eight cycles per minute. And for me, that was conclusive, but I think the research struggled in the development of the machine and there wasn't much follow up after that series of investigations.

Reading the Frymann paper, I also saw that they had a lot of struggles with that kind of measurement because there are so many movements of the human body and it is possible to get confused if you cannot separate them (1971). This also became one of our biggest challenges, but our location in time allowed better technology.

LAH: Yes, let's talk about your machine. You attached sensors to the mastoid process of the temporal bone on either side of the subject's head and you recorded data about their relative movement away from each other and toward each other – were the sensors like calipers attached to each other? Can you describe the apparatus for us?

TRR: The sensors are not attached to each other, they are two independent sensors, it was the software and the computer that calculated their relative motion. The sensors we had on the participants' heads are called servo actuators and you can program the amount of pressure they apply to the head. Even when the head was expanding, normally a machine would have an increase in pressure and the head would meet resistance, but here the machine is programmed to keep the same pressure on the participant's skin, no matter where it moves. This is important, we had the same pressure regardless of movement. We programmed it to be ten grams of pressure. The machine had minimal interference with the participant's head and they reported they didn't really feel the machine on their head. The sensors, they are programmed to be on that spot, so no matter where the head moves around, the sensors will follow the head and keep a ten-gram contact.

We found that there were asymmetries between the left- and right-side movements of the bones. We are going to follow up on that finding and then see if cranial manipulation will change the asymmetry, and we want to investigate if craniosacral therapy will change the amplitude of skull movement.

LAH: So many important avenues to investigate with this technology. The participants didn't need to be strapped down or restrained because the computer could adapt to their regular movements?

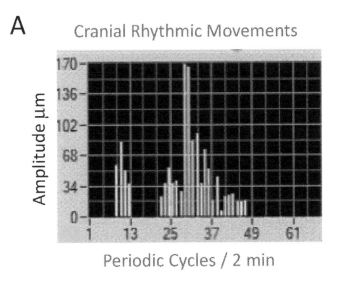

A   Cranial Rhythmic Movements

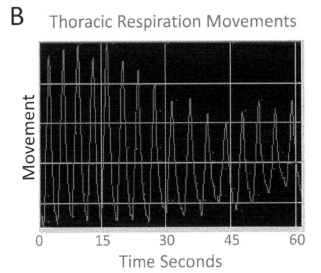

B   Thoracic Respiration Movements

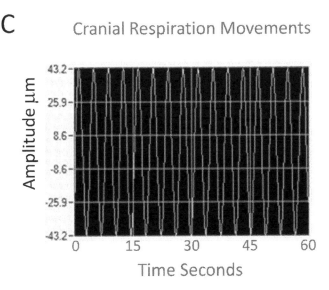

C   Cranial Respiration Movements

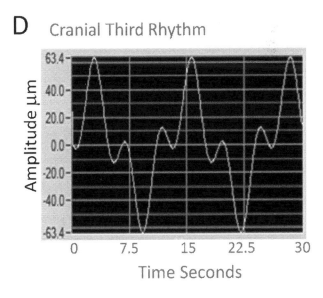

D   Cranial Third Rhythm

Figure 2: Measuring of cranial rhythmic movements and separating a third rhythm from the movements of thoracic respiration. (A) Frequency of cranial movement in relation to time on the x-axis and amplitude of the movement on the y-axis. Two clusters of movement observed, one averaged thirty-five cycles per minute and the second was observed at four to six cycles per minute. (B) Respiratory movement measured at the respiratory diaphragm for a single person over a period of sixty seconds. This individual's respiration was sixteen cycles per minute. (C) Rhythmic movements of respiration measured in the cranium movements matches the sixteen cycles per minute. (D) The third rhythm. It is rhythmic movement in the narrow cluster of four to six cycles per minute identified in A. This third movement is a wave within a wave function with a 'shoulder' about halfway between maximum and minimum amplitude. Creative Commons license: CC BY-NC-ND 4.0.

TRR: Yes. Participants were lying down on a soft treatment table, they were invited to relax and they reported they didn't feel the measurement tool.

LAH: And you mentioned there was nobody else in the room, so it was just the participant's biofield being measured by the instrumentation.

TRR: Yes, and interestingly, when we had just built the machine and were starting to test it out, we could see that if a client was on the table and a therapist came into the room, it affected the measurement. Knowing this, we knew we had to be very strict so we could record the baseline movement, this study was the ground zero for a group of studies of this kind. Now that we have it published, in the future we can learn what kind of variance would be created by a therapist entering the space of the client and stuff like that.

LAH: This baseline study of yours is essential. To summarize, you had fifty participants, men and women, and they had an age range of eighteen to ninety-two. This is the whole adult lifespan that you covered. And the participants had no knowledge of cranial work; they were fresh.

TRR: Yes, and they were actually easier to measure. We have also found out in our pretests that if you have a therapist lying down on the table, in their head they are thinking about what will happen. If you are cognitively processing while being measured for cranial bone movement, you have a fascial reaction and that does create a lot of disturbance in the measurements. You actually see that in the data.

LAH: When I first read your paper I thought, these researchers must be physicists because there is a lot of math and physics in how this investigation was done. You're a medical researcher. You and your team, you built the machine for this type of investigation.

TRR: We built it completely from scratch and the sensors are robot technology. When you have robots that need to do something, then you need to know the exact distance of movement for robotic arms. And the robot needs to know the exact pressure and it needs to control all movements. So, we took the sensors from robot technology and then integrated it with complex software to try to deal with all these variables.

LAH: That's so smart. You're providing an important piece of the puzzle for us practitioners as we communicate with medical colleagues. It is hard to convey that the physical interventions manual therapists are doing are interacting with this third rhythm. That there is a third rhythm of the head and body, that it is something we can palpate, and it's something that we are working with to alleviate discomfort. Up until now, I haven't had a paper that I can point to with my physician clients and say, "Here it is, the third rhythm characterized and published."

TRR: Yes, right, and it's also been very helpful for educating therapists, because when I teach now, I am even more clear about what they have in their hands. I encourage them to distinguish between when they feel the third rhythm, from the breathing movements and arterial pulse. You can feel it everywhere in the body when your palpation skills are increasing, but in the beginning, we say, "Okay, you want to actually feel the two different rhythms," meaning the difference between respiration in the thorax from the third rhythm. They are close together in their cycle frequency.

We have done clinical explorations where we invited very experienced craniosacral therapists and we blindfolded them while they were palpating the cranium. And then we asked, "What do you feel?" We could see from our live data from the head sensors when they were reporting feeling the breathing cycle and we could confirm for them when they were differentiating that from the different rhythmic movement of the third rhythm. We gave them instant feedback while palpating.

LAH: So cool, what a great way to learn. Let's talk about the results of this particular investigation. You reported your results as frequencies of cycles per minute (see Figure 1A). People breathe about fifteen to forty times a minute, where there is individual difference between people. You graphed the frequency of movement in relation to time on the x-axis and the amplitude of the movement on the y-axis, or range of excursion. So, we can see a cluster of movements between fifteen to forty cycles per minute clearly – that's the head being moved by the person's breathing. And slower than that, there is a second peak from four to thirteen cycles per minute. Am I seeing that correctly?

TRR: Yes.

LAH: And that slower rhythm is the third rhythm that was observed with each participant?

TRR: Yes, we had a second measuring device on the body detecting the respiration movements on top of the respiratory diaphragm (see Figure 1B), so the breathing movements in the head were detected (see Figure 1C) and confirmed with the thoracic breathing movements. We observed variation in people's breathing, even when they were lying down. When we looked at head movement there was something else other than this. There was actually a rhythm that is slower than breathing (see Figure 1D).

The breathing rhythm is a beautiful sigmoid curve. When we looked at this third rhythm, it was slower and it could be recognized by a completely different movement pattern.

LAH: Fascinating, such important information. I'm hanging on to the idea about differentiating palpating the breathing movement at the head compared to this third rhythm. They are close together in their cycles per minute, but the third rhythm is differentiated by both being slower and not being a simple sigmoid curve.

What is the wave nature of the third rhythm?

TRR: It is a wave within a wave.

LAH: The mastoid processes were measured to be moving away from each other, that was the peak of the high amplitude part of the graph. Then the mastoid processes start moving toward each other to a middle zone, where the movement turns around for a moment, and then the mastoid processes move away from each other again. They do this just for a little bit of time, that must be the smallest of spaces, and then the movement turns around again as it were, and the space between the mastoid processes decreases quite a bit to an inferior peak. These low peaks are the smallest distance measured between the mastoid processes. The movement amplitude then starts to increase. And again at the middle zone, the area on the mastoid processes neither at their widest, nor at their closest, do this second expand away and narrow together with a small amplitude, before then taking the long trip back up to the widest amplitude peak.

How did you make sense of that?

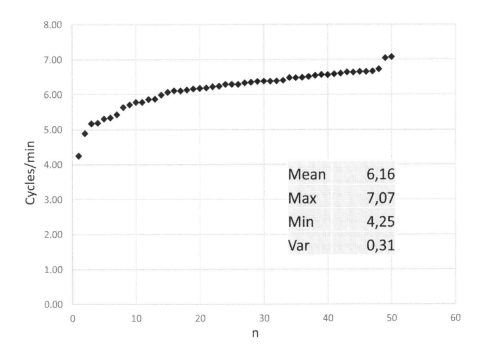

Figure 3: The average (mean) rate of the third rhythm for each participant in the study (n=50). Range of third rhythm of the cranium is from four to seven cycles per minute. Creative Commons license: CC BY-NC-ND 4.0.

TRR: We looked very closely at this detail because in cranial studies, especially from Sutherland, it is all based on this flexion/extension movement, with a neutral zone in the middle. As practitioners, when we are palpating, we feel this stopping or shift, in the middle as you said. With our hands we can feel that as distinct from the flexion to extension. We were very interested to actually measure this. Then we designed the software so we could try to really look in detail at this wave function. What we realized is that by laws of physics and looking at wave functions, this is a wave within a wave. Why is there a wave within a wave? We don't know, but we are very interested, as this might give a clue as to where the wave is coming from.

We compared this third rhythm wave form with the idea of understanding the waves on a cardiogram that have a very complex movement. We are at the beginning of this study; we are curious to find out. It is a part of physiology, and when we see this wave pattern, it is giving us a clue. That is what we are looking into now, how is the wave of this rhythm shaped. Perhaps there is a shifting where these waves are produced or something is interfering, one wave source on top of another wave. In theory, this third rhythm could be the product of two different things going on in the body, but they always follow each other. And so, they're very close.

Whatever generates it, this wave inside a wave is a clue and that is what we are trying to follow.

LAH: That graph (Figure 1D) is interesting to look at, to see the wave on a wave shape you measured, I want to superimpose that knowledge on what I feel between my hands while working. Of course, I want to assign meaning to this, I want to say to myself, the choroid plexus is producing the cerebrospinal fluid and this expansion is perhaps the one aspect of this wave where the mastoid processes move away from each other. And then the downstream absorption of cerebrospinal fluid being the part of the wave where the mastoid processes are their closest, with that inner wave as the neutral zone. Is that what you, perhaps, think it is?

TRR: This comes down to a very core question, and that is, is it the cerebrospinal fluid, and the physiology of this liquid form, that creates the movement, or, do we have a mechanism that makes this movement in the liquid? Which one comes first or what is generating what?

And of course, we look into a lot of brain research regarding cerebrospinal spinal fluid circulation in the brain. What you can see from that is that even the production of cerebrospinal fluid by the choroid plexus is controlled by many mechanisms, including the higher sympathetic tone. Autonomic nervous

system balance influences cerebrospinal fluid production. We have cilia that sit on the lining of the ventricles that can move cerebrospinal fluid in a certain direction when it wants to do that. The movement of the cerebrospinal fluid in the third ventricle is controlled largely by a hormone that generates cilia movement.

Brain scientists have actually put a camera inside the third ventricle and there you can see the cilia are moving. And if you are blocking this hormone, you're blocking the cilia movement, and then by extension, you are blocking the movement of cerebrospinal fluid.

Movement in the fourth ventricle has also been measured where you can see in daytime, when people are walking and talking, the pulsing of the cerebrospinal fluid follows our breathing rhythm. But when people go into deep sleep, their brains shift to a different brainwave pattern, the cerebrospinal fluid falls to a very slow wave, but it creates more fluid movement. So that relates to how important deep sleep is for cerebrospinal fluid movement around the brain. How that relates to stress when there is a lack of deep sleep is something to think about, perhaps it plays a role in developing Alzheimer's disease.

LAH: This is great information. Another finding that I thought was unexpected was that this third rhythm didn't have

Everyone can look at this study and see we have something measured and it is different from respiration and heart rhythm. We have to be careful what we call it or we have to define clearly what we associate it with.

a lot of variation between individuals compared to the variation of their breath. When it came to the cycles per minute, everyone was almost the same, in a small range (see Figure 3). Did I see that right?

TRR: Yes. But also, look at this other graph (see Figure 4). You can see it is measurements from three individuals while they are lying down for forty-two minutes. The person with the highest rate, they also had the bigger variation. The correlation between the variation in the rhythm and the rate of the rhythm was quite strong. It seems that these high-rhythm people had more superficial, fast breathing, but a fifty-person study was not large enough to determine that part.

Our new study also looks at this to define the relationship on a larger scale, relating the third rhythm to breathing and to see if this relates to a basic autonomic nervous system setting. The third rhythm will not go quickly up and down; if you measure the

average rhythm of a person and you do it next week and next week and next week again, it'll be in the same range. And the mean measure [the average] would also be the same under the same conditions of measurement, relaxing awake.

LAH: In the paradigm of Rolfing® Structural Integration, we tend to think about clients as on a spectrum of fascial tension, or tonality is a word we like to use, between hypertonus, where their fascia is generally tight and perhaps feels like shrink wrap to touch, versus hypotonality where people have a lot of fluidity, at the extreme it can even be too much. When I read that part in your article about the lower cycles per minute relating to less movement of the temporal bones, it made me think, perhaps that is their fascial system wholistically just really tightly wrapped? Perhaps hypertonality generally would be most related to the smaller amplitude of movement between the mastoid processes?

TRR: If you think of the fascia, then think of the amplitude of the skull. Think of the superficial fascia around the skull. If we think of that tightness, we can say it may be a clue to what we are going after here. What would be important for the clinical studies is the amplitude of the skull movement. If you look at the amplitude of the skull movement in Figure 5, that is where the big variation is between participants and that could be closely related to the hypertonus/hypotonus of fascia in the Rolfing paradigm.

When we compare amplitude of the relaxed state between clients, then practitioners can feel the fascial system of the body and feel a very core part of the fascial system, and that's going to be easiest with people with the big amplitude. Then a practitioner feels a tight fascial system, and their client has a very low head amplitude when palpated. As practitioners, we come across clients with this presentation, they can have

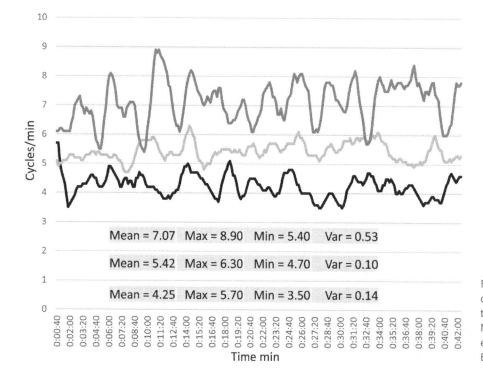

Mean = 7.07 Max = 8.90 Min = 5.40 Var = 0.53

Mean = 5.42 Max = 6.30 Min = 4.70 Var = 0.10

Mean = 4.25 Max = 5.70 Min = 3.50 Var = 0.14

Figure 4: Dynamic nature of the third rhythm during rest of the three persons who represent the highest, lowest, and mid-range rhythm. Mean, max, min, and variance are given for each person. Creative Commons license: CC BY-NC-ND 4.0.

asymmetry and a tight skull. If you try to move the fascia, it doesn't really want to move. And that hypothetical client, say they have very low flexibility in the fascial system in general, this is how you mean that they have a low amplitude.

LAH: Yes, you get my thinking.

TRR: Yes, so the amplitude of the skull you can say from a clinical perspective is a very important part because that's where you see the instant effect of a fascial reaction from manual therapy, because we know that cranial manipulation is a fascial treatment. When you do something with the fascia of the central nervous system, as you're doing craniosacral work, you shift the amplitude very quickly.

LAH: That is the meaning that Rolfers often make when we are making our fascial interventions. To have yourself and your lab group investigating it is very exciting.

You mentioned that in the paper, the past research about the cranial rhythmic impulse was primarily done experientially based on investigations where practitioners were reporting their palpation findings, but this was not received well by the scientific community due to the variation of practitioner skill and the subjective nature of that type of inquiry. We already touched on this, that the palpation of the primary respiratory motion was often done by practitioners monitoring the sphenoid-occiput movement, and to quote your paper it said, "Palpating only for the expansion and retraction may often lead to palpation of respiratory-generated movements . . . As the visceral pharyngeal basilar fascia is attached on this sphenoid/occiput area, the degree of respiratory-transmitted movements to the head may depend on the tension in this visceral fascial system" (Rasmussen and Meulengracht 2021, 28).

Are you saying there that this particular fascia transmits the breath movement to the sphenoid and the practitioner is not feeling a pure third rhythm at the sphenoid because of it? And, is that why you chose to put your sensors on the temporal bones, to bypass that?

TRR: No, because you can say the movement will reflect into all of the skull. So we did test if we move the sensors around the skull, will we have the same rhythm, and we investigated whether we would get different amplitudes. But the reason why we chose the mastoid

was because it's a very easy fix point for everyone to lock the sensors on. We could repeatedly lock them the same way between people. If you go up on the skull, you start to have differences in the skull, and it becomes more difficult to say we are on the same point. That was very important, not for the rate of the rhythm, but more for the studies of amplitude.

The part that you bring up about the fascia is because we can say the whole Sutherland's concept is based on the movement of the sphenoid. If you look at the fascia systems that affect the skull,

> ## "Palpating only for the expansion and retraction may often lead to palpation of respiratory-generated movements . . . As the visceral pharyngeal basilar fascia is attached on this sphenoid/occiput area, the degree of respiratory-transmitted movements to the head may depend on the tension in this visceral fascial system" (Rasmussen and Meulengracht 2021, 28).

the pharyngeal basilar fascia has a very strong attachment on the sphenoid, that is central in osteopathy and craniosacral work. And we say to ourselves, okay, we have a strong fascia sitting here that affects the whole head movement. I did a series of sessions with people with asthma. For people who have suffered real asthma for years, every time they breathe, everything on the head follows that movement because the fascial system is tight. Because you have a tight fascial system, it transmits respiratory breathing movement strongly into the skull; as a practitioner you really have to focus to bypass that breathing movement and feel the third rhythm, because the respiratory breathing can be such a strong movement in the asthmatic situation.

This is our explanation, because some people have a very light fascial system that is very elastic, and then the biggest contribution to the movement of the

head is the third rhythm. But if you have someone where their system is tight, then you can say the movement will be very influenced by respiratory breathing, and you'll feel that readily on the skull.

LAH: What great information. I really appreciate how you're cautious in your language in the paper. You focus on the term: third rhythm. Is that because it isn't yet known what the source of the third rhythm is? How do you teach practitioners to speak about this concept?

TRR: This is my recommendation when different schools are in contact with me, they want to take the conclusions one step ahead like you mentioned, and I turn it around and I say, "The reason why we call it the third rhythm is to keep it open for everyone. We have measured something. If your school wants to call it something, you are welcome to do that, but you need to define what you mean." We can call it the craniosacral rhythm and if you say that the third rhythm is the craniosacral rhythm, then you need to define it from that. We don't know what is moving here. Is it the fascia contraction? Bones moving? We don't know. So, we have to be honest and say, we can conclude on what we have measured here, but we cannot draw the conclusion further than that. Everyone can look at this study and see we have something measured and it is different from respiration and heart rhythm. We have to be careful what we call it or we have to define clearly what we associate it with.

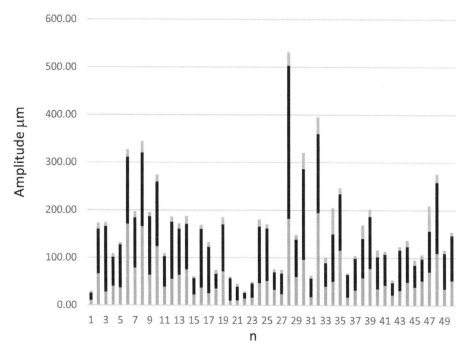

Figure 5: The amplitude of all three rhythmic head movements originating from the arterial pulsation, respiratory breathing, and the third rhythm were measured in micrometers. Grey bar on top = arterial pulse generated amplitude, black = respiratory breathing generated amplitude, and grey bar below = third rhythm generated amplitude. Creative Commons license: CC BY-NC-ND 4.0.

We need to think differently if we want our profession to develop and we want to be as clear as possible when we speak and when we teach. It becomes important when we want to speak between different schools or when we want to speak with the medical society. We can be clear in what we are saying, and I think fascia research in general is very interesting. For many schools, including yours, fascia research is very important for understanding the actual phenomena of the body, and fascia research informs how we develop what we do.

LAH: So well said, it's an exciting time to be doing this work because of the increasing volume of fascia research, now we have peer-reviewed work as our baseline of 'normal' function. As practitioners, we are able to learn from researchers, like you, and paying careful attention to our language is so important. The variable called the third rhythm is a new language for me and I'm going to use it liberally. It is important that we have a common language that's agreeable between disciplines.

You already mentioned a little bit about the relationship of the third rhythm and the autonomic nervous system, you related it to having changes between walking compared to sleeping. My own lens when I think about autonomic nervous system functioning, I think about sympathetic and parasympathetic arousal levels, as Rolfers we often think about fight, flight, and freeze. Do you think the third rhythm has variation around these kinds of arousal states?

TRR: I would believe so, but I don't have the data. I have a sense that what we have seen in the data is that the third rhythm is more a long-term setting. Let's say my brainstem, due to whatever I experience as trauma in my life, more easily goes into the red-alert trauma field. So, I will be running on a fight or flight responses very easily. Then my base setting in my autonomic system is high. We know that if you have a client and their base setting is very high, it will often be a long-term process to shift the brainstem setting to be in less frequently in the red zone. But maybe many sessions can support the baseline autonomic function to a more flexible setting.

LAH: Exactly.

TRR: I think that the third rhythm has some kind of relation to that and we will see a more long-term pattern. Breathing can do this in a clearly palpable and observable rate. The cardiac rhythm can do a quick response, but the third rhythm is a more long-term setting. When we see people with a more superficial breathing and that they are alert, they have a tendency to have a higher arousal rate. Whereas, the people who have deeper and more flexible breathing, they have a tendency toward a lower rate. It's only a tendency that we see. Like all the other basic life rhythms, they have at least some part of their control from the brainstem. And we know that the cranial or third rhythm is out of our cognitive control. You cannot control it.

LAH: Your article is just the big beginning of so many great questions. What kinds of things are your research team looking at next?

TRR: We can say what's coming out in 2022. We will look at physiological experiments where we are pressing the human body to its extremes while we are measuring the third rhythm. We are redesigning the equipment for that because you need to measure someone who is moving. So, we will look at what happens when people perform at their maximum output and what will happen when they go from that to deep relaxation.

LAH: From running to stillness.

TRR: Yes. And what happens when you force the breathing, if you hyperventilate to almost fainting states. So that's one part of what we are looking at. Then we have done a very long-term clinical study to see the long-term effects of craniosacral therapy on the rhythm, on the amplitudes and the skull, because as a practitioner, as you said yourself, you feel that if you have this completely frozen fascia system, or you feel that tightness and tension in the fascia, will that actually change when you follow the person over time and will that change affect the amplitude of movement of the skull? And the major thing that we are interested in here is finding out if we can affect the cerebrospinal fluid circulation with manual interventions. For me, I see that as a very important part in the future, because of the exponential increase in neurodegenerative disorders like Alzheimer's and all kinds of dementia.

LAH: Yes, this is the heart of it. Your work is directly expanding the knowledge we have and it's gratifying to think about this now clearly defined third rhythm and the relationships that may now be observed, the important questions to ask. Thank you so much for helping me and our readers get up-to-date with this current knowledge. Great research, thank you for explaining it to us.

TRR: You're welcome. Hopefully all the different aspects we have from fascia, physiology, and central nervous system research come together in manual therapy and we can be a major part of the future of health care.

Thomas Rosenkilde Rasmussen, PhD, MSC, CST-D, is a Danish researcher and craniosacral therapy practitioner. He has a PhD in medicine from University of Copenhagen, a master's of science degree in chemistry, a bachelor's degree in biochemistry, and another bachelor's degree in biology. For fifteen years Rasmussen worked as a scientist in cancer research, working in different parts of the world including Canada, United States, and Japan. Part of Rasmussen's research was with hematological cancers. He also has a focus on the craniosacral system, as he is an instructor with the Upledger Institute International, and the Director of Research for Upledger Institute International.

Lina Amy Hack, BS, BA, SEP, became a Rolfer in 2004 and is now a Certified Advanced Rolfer (2016) practicing in Saskatoon, Saskatchewan, Canada. She has an honors biochemistry degree from Simon Fraser University (2000) and an honors psychology degree from the University of Saskatchewan (2013), as well as a Somatic Experiencing® Practitioner (2015) certification. Hack is the Editor-in-Chief of Structure, Function, Integration.

References

Frymann, Viola M. 1971. A study of the rhythmic motions of the living cranium. *The Journal of the American Osteopathic Association* 70(9): 928-945.

Rasmussen, Thomas Rosenkilde, and Karl Christian Meulengracht. 2021. Direct measurement of the rhythmic motions of the human head identifies a third rhythm. *Journal of Bodywork and Movement Therapies* 26:24-29.

Sutherland, W. G. 1939. *The cranial bowl.* Mankato, Minnesota: Free Press Co.

Letter from the Embryo

Home, Straight Home

By Konrad Obermeier, Basic Rolfing® Instructor

Konrad Obermeier

ABSTRACT *From the perspective of the embryo, Konrad Obermeier writes about the development of the midline, the tissues that become the axial complex. The notochord develops in a context of growth differentials, Obermeier describes this beginning of the longitudinal line that leads to human verticality.*

To manifest and maintain a four-dimensional human territory is an amazing endeavor. Every fertilized human ovum performs this extraordinary process by orchestrating growth and differentiation into form.

Obviously, every single cell is participating in this process and is flowing as a local event through the moment-by-moment continuity of development. The general expansive potential of growth is expressed locally and transitorily by all cells. Growth manifests in innumerable nuances and is locally modified by the environment. At all times growth is an *out-side-in* process: available molecular substances from the *out-side* are *in*corporated and assimilated into the organism.

All cells collectively hold identical genetic information but respond to the immediacy of the environmental circumstances individually. A cell is metabolically stimulated or restrained and spaciously enabled or restricted. The form of a cell demonstrates adaptability when volume is deformed, compressed, or dilated by forces of pressure and tension. A cell is capacitated or inhibited towards multiplication; fed in the morning,

starving at night; suspended and in need of molecular support or in high gear and pluri-performing on the spot. Every single cell in every moment is absolutely woven into the fabric of highly specific environmental circumstances. Cells in areas of momentarily fast expansion are in direct contact and meet ('skin to skin', as it were) groups of almost hibernating cells in areas of slow growth. Packs of cells that manifest an almost explosive run-away reproductive potential relate to timid tissues of retarded reproduction rates.

Within a short time of developmental movement in the tiniest of areas these vectorial relationships may start or stop, intensify or slow down, continue or reverse.

Growth rates are highly variable and a central aspect of manifesting structure, shape, form, and contour.

Biodynamic embryology proposes the idea that the variability of cellular growth-rates is in relationship to the relative position of the cell in its immediate surrounding. This idea originates from the simple but often overlooked observation that cells can basically find themselves in two different topographic positions:

Figure 1: Midline formation is the initial and pivotal moment in which internal-tissue (IT) arises from the concentric folding of layers of limiting-tissue (LT). 1. Amnion, 2. Yolk sac, 3. Chorion, 4. Placenta. Illustrations are redrawn from originals, all from different publications by Dr. Erich Blechschmidt, used with permission.

At all times growth is an *out-side-in* process: available molecular substances from the *out-side* are *in*corporated and assimilated into the organism.

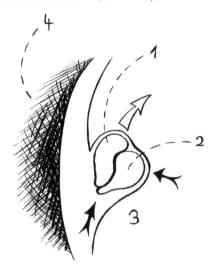

1. Cells that are relating directly to a fluid filled space, then they are called *'limiting-tissue'* (LT). LT-cells manifest relative high growth rates.

2. Cells that are surrounded by other cells and do not directly relate to a fluid filled space, then they are called *'internal-tissue'* (IT). IT-cells are embedded in the matrix of the ground

substance and demonstrate relative slow growth rates.

Midline formation is the initial and pivotal moment in which IT arises from the concentric folding of layers of LT. Visualize the surfaces of two fluid-filled balloons in contact with each other (see Figure 1), this is like the amnion and yolk sac. The surfaces in touch with each other represent single layers of LT-cells. When the surface layers of these balloons fold up on each other in three dimensions, some cells will be caught up between the LT-layers and folded in by the biodynamic developmental origami; they will find themselves surrounded by cells and hence they will no longer have direct access to a fluid cavity (see Figure 2).

The birth of the midline corresponds with the initial arising of IT, resulting in the appearance of the first metabolic fulcrum,

a still dynamic but relatively stable 'slow-growth-area', localizing the cranial base as a starting point. The axial elongation of this metabolic density will manifest the notochord. The structure of the spine is just a developmental consequence of this transitory preconditions (Blechschmidt would use the word *anlage*) with the segmentation into vertebral units originating from arterial intersections providing rhythmic molecular support for cellular clusters. These groups of cells will later differentiate into bones, ligaments, muscles, discs, and all the rest of specific tissues that comprise a single vertebra.

Midline IT demonstrates a slower growth rate than the relating LT and so introduces relative resistance to expansive forces of growth. To paraphrase this: IT dynamics are to LT dynamics as a coachman's reins are to his horses. The former directs and orients the latter by restraining them. The expansive growth of LT is organized by

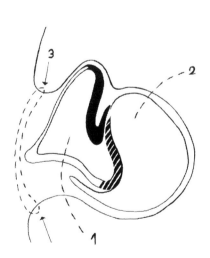

Figure 2: Folding of surface layers on each other. 1. Amnion, 2. Yolk sac, 3. Connecting stalk. Illustrations are redrawn from originals, all from different publications by Dr. Erich Blechschmidt, used with permission.

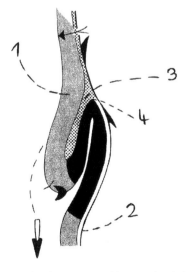

Figure 3: Axial process with notochord in black (lateral view). 1. LT growth dynamics of ectoderm, 2. LT growth resistance of endoderm, 3. IT first mesoderm, 4. Tip of axial process. Illustrations are redrawn from originals, all from different publications by Dr. Erich Blechschmidt, used with permission.

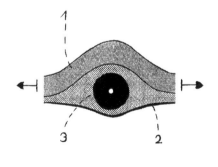

Figure 4: Axial process with notochord in black (transverse view). 1. Ectodermal LT – vertical cell arrangement, 2. Endodermal LT – horizontal cell arrangement, 3. Mesodermal IT. Illustrations are redrawn from originals, all from different publications by Dr. Erich Blechschmidt, used with permission.

The notochord introduces an axiality, a basic longitude as the original foundation of verticality. The notochord provides a stabilizing function for the metabolic and dynamic processes of developmental movement and structure.

and in relationship to the relative inertia of IT. James Jealous, DO, refers to this with the words (Horrigan 1997): *"The midline is . . . a primary line of orientation for all spatial dynamics."*

We propose the idea here that what holds true for the developmental movement and growth dynamics of the embryo also holds true for structural dynamics and structural maintenance of the post-natal embryo. From the initial development of the primary IT, all further organization of the voluminous three-dimensional territory of the body will continuously relate to this dynamic fulcrum (see Figure 3 and 4).

The differentiation into all kinds of tissue types will take this first folding of LT into IT as the naturally arising origin and center of expansion. The notochord lays down a stabilizing and dynamic template within the embryo. This anchoring template functions like a musical theme in an opera, that is then realized, implemented, rehearsed, and executed in different domains of tissues.

The locomotive system, the visceral system, and the nervous system in their early manifestation all orient towards this longitudinal axis (see Figure 5).

The notochord introduces an axiality, a basic longitude as the original foundation of verticality. The notochord provides a stabilizing function for the metabolic and dynamic processes of developmental movement and structure. Prior to cognitive naming and labeling, the embryo now owns a home-base with corresponding orientation and vectoriality. The peripheries, with their own growth dynamics, also refer to and originate from this axis.

Indeed, this axis is the primary orientation for girdles and extremities, their developmental movement being guided by neuro-vascular bundles. In fact, the whole of senso-motricity that we understand as *hapticity as a process* that relates directly to this directional 'home', it is internalized and ingested and reviewed there. The embryo, as well as the post-natal embryo, organizes all her motor-

sensorial *in-side-out* answers towards the world from this home base of the midline. The integrated process we call midline is expressing itself as tonic function.

As pre-natal and post-natal embryos always know:

A truly functioning functional midline is like a mirror:

Out-side-in / In-side-out.

Konrad Obermeier holds a degree in communications from the University of Munich and has been a Rolfer® since 1991. Currently, he serves as chair of the anatomy faculty for the European Rolfing® Association. He is the editor of a series of books on the biodynamic embryology of Erich Blechschmidt.

References

Horrigan, Bonnie. 1997 Jan. Jim Jealous, DO – Healings and the natural world. *Alternative Therapies in Health and Medicine* Vol 3(1):68-76.

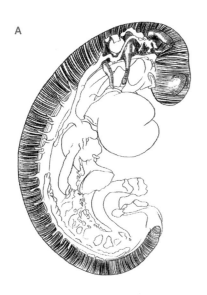 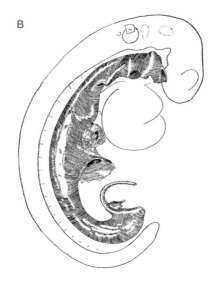 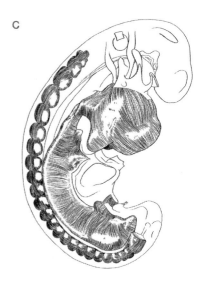

Figure 5: Neural home (A), Visceral home (B), and Motor home (C). Illustrations are redrawn from originals, all from different publications by Dr. Erich Blechschmidt, used with permission.

The Cord Canal Ride

by Kathy McConnell, Certified Advanced Rolfer®, Rolf Movement Practitioner®

Ladies and gentlemen
Facets and foramens
Come one come all
To our grand celebration!

It's truly my pleasure
As I stand here before you
To honor a structure
Of miraculous proportion.

Where else than the spine
Can you possibly find
Such complex
And dynamic mechanics?

Praise to erectors
Those sinews and tissues
Iliocostales
Multifidus, spinales.

With pulleys and wires
And fluids galore
Homeostasis
is right at the fore.

From dens to coccyx
Way deep inside
A liquid light show
The cord canal ride.

Take refuge in movement
Exploring this zone
Rocking and swaying
From bone to bone.

Off to the races
In search of new spaces
Watching the sparkles
Along the way.

It's said luminescence
Is really our essence
Keeping us shining
Come what may.

Glamor and glitz
Luster and sheen
Try it yourself
See what I mean!

Kathy McConnell

Kathy McConnell is a Certified Advanced Rolfer and Rolf Movement Practitioner in the San Francisco Bay Area. During her twenty years of practice she has assembled an eclectic palette of formal and self-directed trainings that influence her work, including craniosacral work, medical qigong, and Western esoteric studies. Through her poetry she is experimenting with the language of embodiment that is awakened by Rolfing® Structural Integration and Rolf Movement.

Your Spine Is Not a Column

An Excerpt from *Your Body Mandala*

By Mary Bond, Rolf Movement® Instructor Emeritus

Mary Bond

ABSTRACT *In this article, which is a chapter excerpted from* Your Body Mandala *(2018), Mary Bond explores the nature of the human spine, the evolutionary journey that led to the various movements capable by the spine, and the variability of shape observed within individual spines. Bond describes the sacrum clock movement exercise and how to visualize accessing the movement of the coccyx.*

Editor's note: This article is an excerpt (Chapter 9) from Mary Bond's book Your Body Mandala *(2018: MCP Books, Maitland, Florida, reprinted with permission). We have made modifications for our journal style.*

The concept that the spine is a column stems from the mechanical model of the body. In fact, your spine functions like a tensegrity tower – it is more akin to Kenneth Snelson's Needle Tower in Washington, D.C., than it is to the Washington Monument (see Figure 1).

Your vertebrae are suspended in your fascial matrix like a string of pearls, not stacked up like blocks. Fascial tissues weave in and around the spinal segments, securing them, but also holding them apart. This prevents the vertebral bodies from bearing down upon one another and causing erosion. The 'pearls' are more or less mobile, depending on the elasticity of the fascial weaving.

The subtle lengthening of your spine that you feel when you inhale gives you a sense of the labile nature of your spine. If you haven't been able to feel that as yet, this chapter should help.

Evolutionary Journey

In a healthy spine, the vertebrae are configured into shallow forward and backward curves (see Figure 2). It's a commonly accepted hypothesis that these curves are a product of life's evolutionary journey from sea to land some 450 million years ago. The assumption is that primitive fish moved in the same way as modern fish, with a sideways undulation of their spines (Gracovetsky 1988). This sidebending is a movement your own spine does whenever you reach one hand above your head – to change a light bulb, for example.

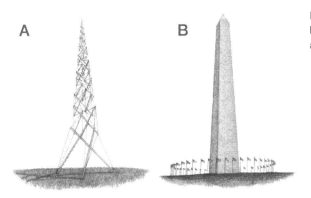

A   B

Figure 1: Your spine is more like a tensegrity tower (A) than an obelisk (B).

Spinal Mobility

If a medical professional applies the terms *kyphosis* or *lordosis* to you, don't worry. These are words used to describe *normal* spinal curvatures (see Figure 3). Kyphosis indicates the natural forward curve or slight flexion of your thoracic spine. Lordosis describes the backward curves or slight extension of your neck and lower back. Curves in the spine are problematic only when they're not adaptive – when they can't curve into the opposite direction. For example, a *thoracic* kyphosis that has become encased in stiffened fascia would be unable to extend and rotate. A movement such as reaching for something behind the body – into the back seat of your car, perhaps – could strain the spine. Even more likely, the spinal stiffness would cause the shoulder to overstretch, injuring the shoulder. To prevent that happening again, you'd need to improve the mobility of your spine.

When our hypothetical fish first emerged from the oceans, they had to plant their fins into the mud in order to lift their bodies over pebbles and other obstacles. This lifting involved rotating their spines. The combination of sideways undulation with the new axial rotation gave rise to forward and backward movements. (You can feel this for yourself: if you bend your torso sideways and then twist, one side of your spine will be subtly flexing and the other side extending. The more you flex or extend, the farther you will be able to rotate. This is known as *coupled motion of the spine*.)

Over the eons, as creatures ventured into varied terrain, they developed increasingly adaptive structures – limbs and paws to gain better purchase on the ground, hips and shoulders for additional power. Evolution of a spine capable of flexion, extension, and rotation in addition to sidebending, plus the development of sophisticated limbs, allowed complex movements such as clambering across rocky terrain and swinging through forest canopies. Or belly dancing. Or golf.

Or walking. When our bodies have tensional integrity and healthy, resilient fascia, our spines, pelvises, legs, and feet all subtly rotate in order to move us forward. You begin experiencing this in the *foot and spine spirals* practice in Chapter 8 [of *Your Body Mandala* (Bond 2018)].

Echoing the evolutionary path to uprightness, the individual human spine makes a developmental journey. Before birth, your spine was curved in a C shape. When, a few months after birth, you grew strong enough to lift your head, you built the backward curve of the *cervical* or neck vertebrae. By struggling to sit up, you strengthened a second backward curve in the waist or *lumbar* area. The four-legged movements of crawling and creeping were similar to the movements of creatures as they evolved from sea to land. Once standing, the curves in your spine helped absorb the impact of your feet striking the ground.

The spinal curves are normal and necessary. They enable you to move in all three planes. When you flex or extend, you're moving in the sagittal plane. When you twist and turn, you're moving in the horizontal plane. When you rock from side to side, you're moving in the coronal plane. Thus, unlike a fish, you're capable of movement in three dimensions. This adaptability of the human spine lets you function in the field of gravity. Whether you're hiking over mountain scree, playing tennis, or dancing a tango, the relationship between your adaptable spine and your adaptable feet gives your body its sustainability and grace.

The base of your spine, the triangular-shaped *sacrum*, is moored between twin pelvic bones. Although this makes the pelvis look solid, it is anything but a stable platform. Not only can the pelvis twist within itself, it is poised over two round knobs, like ball bearings, at the hip joints. When unrestricted, the hips allow considerable rocking and swaying of the pelvis. This built-in instability of the lower half of your body is what lets you freely move about. Your spine should be adaptable enough to respond to the mobility of your hips, legs, and feet.

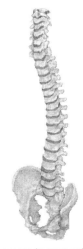

Figure 2: The curves in your spine are natural and necessary. They contribute to your spine's springiness.

Your vertebrae are suspended in your fascial matrix like a string of pearls, not stacked up like blocks. Fascial tissues weave in and around the spinal segments, securing them, but also holding them apart.

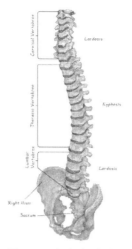

Figure 3: The cervical lordosis, thoracic kyphosis, and lumbar lordosis curvatures pictured with the sacrum and ilium.

Mobilizing the Spine's Foundation

The practice in this chapter contributes to improved mobility between the lower vertebral segments and your sacrum, and between the sacrum, the pelvis, and the hip joints.

You'll start at the base of the spine, heightening awareness of the way the sacrum can articulate with its neighboring pelvic bones, the *ilia*. Through this practice you restore mobility to the pelvis and facilitate greater freedom in your hip joints. You begin to sense the elasticity present within your pelvis, and the fascial connectivity of your pelvis, legs, and spine.

Take plenty of time – weeks rather than days – to explore the sequence of practices in this chapter and the next. Each one offers you improved self-support, adaptability, centeredness, and grace.

Sacred Bone

Your sacrum and ilia rest against one another at the *sacroiliac joints*. The ilia swivel back and forth with every step. Although the amount of rotation at the sacroiliac joint is tiny, it can make a big difference in the capacity of the pelvis to convey helical motion between the legs and spine while you're walking.

Your sacroiliac joints are capable of moving back and forth about two to four millimeters. Although this movement is minute, it is essential for fluid motion of

the lower back and pelvis. The exploration that follows brings awareness to your sacroiliac joints and encourages normal movement there. The practice is an adaptation of an exercise borrowed from the Feldenkrais Method®. Dr. Moshé Feldenkrais, a contemporary of Ida Rolf, PhD, founded a gentle and effective system of movement rehabilitation. His approach utilizes brain plasticity through targeted awareness to restore optimal body organization (Feldenkrais Guild® of North America 2022).

Practice: Preparation for Sacrum Clock

For *sacrum clock* you will need to lie on the floor with your knees flexed at right angles and the soles of your feet resting on a wall. If your upper spine is rounded, place a small lift under your neck and head to keep your airway free.

Lie close enough to the wall that your thighs can be vertical. Position your feet hip distance apart. Scoot them upward about an inch, until your toes are resting just above the level of your knees. Spread your toes apart from each other. Let the pad of each toe make contact with the wall.

Positioning your feet may have brought some tension into your legs. Take a moment to relax your calves while keeping mindful contact of your feet with the wall. Let your feet be *touched* by the wall. Imagine vectors that project from the tops of your shins to the ceiling. These imaginary cables will help your legs relax in this position.

Extend your upper arms outward in line with your armpits. Bend your elbows so your forearms are at right angles with your upper arms. Your arms make the shape of a goalpost on a football field. The backs of your hands rest on the floor. (If your hands don't reach the floor, place folded towels beneath your forearms and hands. The props will make it easier for your shoulders to relax and your chest to expand.)

Allow a slight backward curve or lordosis in your lumbar spine. There will be a tiny puff of air between the floor and your lower back. This is your *neutral lumbar curve*.

Position your head so your eyes gaze straight up at the ceiling. This establishes a neutral curve in your neck. Do not press your neck into the floor to make it straight.

Each time you inhale, feel your upper chest widening – your armpits seem to move apart from each other. When you exhale, let your spine, legs, and head settle ever more deeply into the ground.

As your armpits spread apart from each other, your two elbow points also expand sideways. Each inhalation lengthens the horizontal vector between your elbow points. Gently sustain that expansion as you exhale, and let your head and spine sink deeper into the floor between your elbows.

This breathing practice broadens your back and helps create space for freer movement in your spine.

Sacrum Clock

For this practice, you will imagine a clock face on the front surface of your sacrum. The top of your sacrum is 'twelve o'clock'. Your coccyx is 'six o'clock'. The center of the clock is the neutral resting place for your pelvis (see Figure 4). When your pelvis is neutral, there will be a slight gap between your lumbar area and the ground. There will also be a sense of spaciousness between your coccyx and your sit bones. Look at the illustration of the pelvic floor (see Figure 5). Your coccyx and sit bones border an area called the posterior or *anal triangle* of the pelvic floor. It is behind your perineal point. Try to keep this area spacious during the upcoming practices.

Practice: Sacrum Clock

Lie with your feet on the wall as before, but this time place the palms of your hands on

Whether you're hiking over mountain scree, playing tennis, or dancing a tango, the relationship between your adaptable spine and your adaptable feet gives your body its sustainability and grace.

Imagine a clock face on the front surface of your sacrum. The top of your sacrum is 'twelve o'clock'. Your coccyx is 'six o'clock'. The center of the clock is the neutral resting place for your pelvis

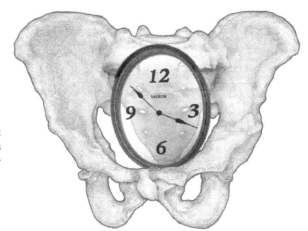

Figure 4: Imagining a clock face on your sacrum helps you release and balance your sacroiliac joints.

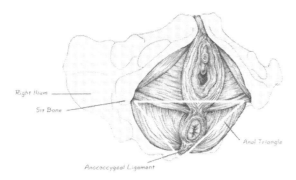

Figure 5: Spaciousness of the anal triangle of the pelvic floor facilitates the best angle for the sacrum, and thereby contributes support for the spinal curves above.

Your hands will ride down when you return to neutral. Notice how your thigh bones then settle back into their sockets. Perhaps one hip settles in more easily than the other. Observe that without wishing for symmetry right now.

From there, continue rolling down beyond neutral into six o'clock. This creates a small arch in your lower back. Your upper back and shoulders continue yielding to the floor. Notice that your thighs now sink even more deeply into your hip sockets.

Once again return to the center of your clock. Pause to soften any tension in your calves, thighs, or pelvic floor.

Softly, slowly, roll back into twelve o'clock. Then return through neutral and roll down into six o'clock. And repeat. Feel the movement of your thighs in your hip sockets as your sacrum rocks back and forth. Then rest in neutral. Check to be sure you are breathing steadily and gently.

This is a good place to pause and rest, or to take a break and continue the practice during another session.

From here, lean your clock face toward three o'clock, toward the left side of your pelvis. And then back to neutral. And now lean your clock face gently into nine o'clock. And back to neutral. You may notice that it's easier to yield into nine or into three.

Next time you move into the stiffer side, pause there. Imagine your thigh bone on that side sinking more deeply into its hip socket. Picture sand pouring into the base of an hourglass. Exhale. And then return again to neutral.

Check that you are still aware of your feet being in contact with the wall and that your calves are soft.

And now begin a slow-motion rocking between three and nine. The movement is so small that someone watching you would not see it. Appreciate the ease with which you yield into the easier side. Be gentle with your wish for the stiffer side to soften.

Notice that as you rest into three o'clock, the nine o'clock side floats slightly upward, away from the floor. As you yield into nine o'clock, the three o'clock side rises.

As you yield again into three o'clock, your left thigh rests back into the hip socket, and your left buttock softens. As you yield into nine o'clock, your right buttock softens, and your thigh bone rests deeper and deeper into the right hip socket.

the tops of your thighs just above your groin. Your upper arms will be resting on the floor close to your sides.

Gently press your feet into the wall. As you do this, let your sacrum tip back toward twelve o'clock. Your neutral lumbar curve will flatten a little. Soften your abdomen and imagine your internal organs resting back into your lumbar area as if into a hammock.

Now, relax the pressure of your feet and let your sacrum return to a neutral place, at the center of your clock. Notice whether the anal triangle of your pelvic floor has narrowed. If it has, let your sit bones and coccyx spread apart, melting

the tension there. Visualize the tiny strand of fascia between your anus and coccyx becoming longer.

Slightly increase the pressure of your feet against the wall, and picture your sit bones staying wide apart. Keep your anal triangle spacious as you repeat the tipping movement of your sacrum.

And again return to neutral.

As you press your feet once more and rest back into twelve o'clock, you will notice that the shift of weight through your pelvis has made your thigh bones move up, taking your hands with them. Your thighs have actually shifted forward in the hip sockets.

Return to the center of your clock, with awareness of the neutral curve in your lumbar spine. Feel the spaciousness of the anal triangle of your pelvic floor. Breathe.

To finish, slide your feet up along the wall, straightening your knees. Reach your arms up above your head. Relax your concentration. Let your body move in any way that feels comfortable.

When you're ready, roll to your side and rest in a fetal curl for a moment.

Then bring yourself up to standing.

Notice how it feels to be upright. Observe how the weight of your body rests through your ankles and into your feet. Notice your sense of presence in this moment. Notice how the world appears to you from this place in yourself.

When you walk, you may be newly aware of your sacrum. Observe how that awareness affects the way you're moving. Perhaps there's a new ease in the way your legs swing under your body into each next step.

Perhaps there's an unexpected shift in your mood.

Tail Space

Poor posture is most obvious in the carriage of your head and shoulders, but in fact, your pelvis is often the literal seat of the problem. When relationships between the pelvic bones and hips are skewed, everything above and below is affected, as you have been able to feel for yourself in the *sacrum clock* practice. The meditation helps you experience your pelvis as a base of operations between your spine and legs.

Tucking the tail under – a habitually backward tilt of the pelvis – provides poor support for the spine, restricts movement at the hip joints, and limits movement of the legs. Although tilting the pelvis back – moving into twelve o'clock, for example – is a normal movement of your pelvis, it is not a healthy place for your pelvis to stay.

Chronic shortening of the myofascia around the anus and the coccyx is one of many reasons for the habit of tucking the tail. Many of us have landed painfully on our coccyxes. We were soaring down the skate path on our rollerblades, and wham! This usually happens when we're having fun. Sitting down becomes a trial for weeks afterward. Guarding the injured area shortens fascia in the posterior triangle of the pelvic floor and embeds new brain mapping of the pelvis.

Many myofascial structures of the pelvic floor and hip joints collaborate in shortening the anal triangle. You can begin to release this area by imagining that the anococcygeal ligament can lengthen. The ligament's location between anus and coccyx makes this easy to picture. The ligament itself may not actually get longer, but the visualization causes structures around it to relax.

Experiment by placing one finger lightly on the tip of your coccyx. If your coccyx has been bent under by a bad landing, you may have to reach your finger forward between your 'cheeks'. After gently locating the tip of your coccyx you can bring your hand away.

Now, without changing anything else about your posture, draw your tail farther forward toward your anus. You are making the tail-tucking pattern worse on purpose, to feel how your tissues contract and to highlight that sensation. Then release, imagine your 'tail space ligament' lengthening and your coccyx moving back away from your anus. The movement is subtle, internal, and should not produce an obvious change in the orientation of your pelvis. But notice how that tiny release of the posterior pelvic floor affects your overall stance – you'll feel securely planted on your feet and upright in your torso. You may even notice an interior lengthening sensation as far upward as your throat.

It will be beneficial to review the clock meditation with this added detail in your awareness. And carry your tail space awareness into the rest of the meditations in the book (Bond 2018).

There are many reasons for tensions and imbalances in the pelvic floor – sexual trauma, traumatic childbirth, and lower bowel congestion, to name a few. Any of these can affect the function of your body as a whole – your movement, posture, and peace of mind. It will benefit your *body mandala* practice to seek professional help for such issues.

The Minute Hand

Many people feel stiffer on the 'nine' or 'three' side of their sacrum clocks, with a stiffer hip joint on the same side. If that is true of you, see whether this pattern correlates to your 'preferred leg', the one you stand on first to put on your pants. The lumbar fascia on that side of your lower back is also likely to be thicker than on the other side. This is both the deep fascial patterning of your personal *contrapposto* (see Chapter 7, Bond 2018) and a habit of your brain.

Once the basic sacrum clock practice feels familiar and easy, you may be able to re-map your asymmetrical pattern by practicing minute-by-minute circuits around your clock face. Begin at 'twelve' and find your way clockwise or counter-clockwise around the hours. Yield into each minute, traveling as slowly as the minute hand. You will likely find there are

. . . draw your tail farther forward toward your anus. You are making the tail-tucking pattern worse on purpose, to feel how your tissues contract and to highlight that sensation. Then release, imagine your 'tail space ligament' lengthening and your coccyx moving back away from your anus.

flat places in your circuit even though the clock face is round. You may also notice hesitations – areas where the movement feels discontinuous rather than smooth. These hesitations indicate that your brain is attempting to map new coordination at your sacroiliac joints. Respect the hesitations. Patient practice will smooth them out.

Coach yourself to yield more deeply into the flat or bumpy areas. You can refresh the yielding sensation by reviewing the *rolling* practice from chapter one (Bond 2018). Also recall the way inhalation creates multidirectional vectors through your body. Use your inhalation to expand your interior space and your exhalation to help you yield. Patient interoception invites stiff and matted fascia to soften so that bony surfaces can decompress.

It does not matter whether you make a perfectly round transit around your clock face. The practice is effective without your having to reach perfection. Stop your practice whenever you begin to feel frustrated. A short period of sincere practice will give you a measure of new coordination, but trying to hurry your body into a new pattern will only create more tension.

Walking Integration

After you stand up, take a walk to notice any effect the sacrum clock practice has had on your legs, hips, and spine. Simply feel. Don't try to analyze it or make something happen. It's fine if you notice nothing at all at first. Creating new movement maps in your brain takes time and patience.[1]

Healthy coordination is intrinsic to your biotensegrity structure. Walking biomechanics involves the way the bones that comprise each joint float against one another in the fascial matrix, the way the various muscles add impetus, and how the entire fascial net supports and facilitates each contributing joint action. Actually, every cell in your body is involved in every moment of every step.

Over time, we all acquire habits that obstruct tensegral coordination. Sacrum clock and other practices [in the book] help you revise those habits. By working with micromovements, you reach the deepest layers of your fascial body and reawaken sensations that your nervous system has forgotten.

Neural plasticity, and the brain's relationship to the body, is highly changeable. According to psychiatrist and neuroscience writer Norman Doidge, MD, walking generates new brain cells and growth factors that strengthen the neural connections involved in learning a new skill (2015). When we feel our bodies differently, we experience our movement differently, and such newly felt movement is a new motor skill.

Reflection: A Random Pain

I wake up early with pain in my left knee. It hurts to bear weight on it. It hurts to use the toilet, hurts to feed the cat, so I don't even consider a morning walk. Random pains like this tend to assert themselves the older I get.

Okay, I decide, I'll do some stretches on the floor; get my juices moving that way. I lie down. Without thinking about it, my feet go up on the wall in position for the clock practice. It's comfortable for them to be there.

The knee pain could be sourced in my pelvis. My sacroiliac joints could be out of alignment and tension resulting from that could irritate nerves that affect the knee. I suspend my shins from their imaginary cables, and slowly travel around my pelvic clock. The movement stutters, especially on the left side, and it takes a while for it to smooth out.

Twenty minutes later I stand up feeling bigger. The knee pain is gone.

What has happened? I can't be sure whether my clock meditation has realigned my pelvic bones and relieved an impinged nerve, or whether the pain was a transient event that resolved on its own. What I can say with confidence is that by paying attention to the spaciousness and yielding of my body on the floor, and to the micromovements of my pelvis, I affected the tensegral expansion of my fascial body as a whole. More often than not, a random pain can be modulated by embodied wholeness. Not only physical pain. I remember my argument with Richard (Chapter 3, Bond 2018) – tuning in to my embodiment transformed that pain as well.

Endnote

1. In *The New Rules of Posture* (Bond 2007) and in my video course, *Heal Your Posture* (Bond 2012), I simplified the

mechanics of walking into incremental joint motions. In *Your Body Mandala* (Bond 2018), my intention is to help you embody your wholeness, rather than to focus on what various parts should be doing while you walk.

Mary Bond has a master's degree in dance from University of California, Los Angeles, and trained with Dr. Ida Rolf as a structural integration practitioner. Formerly chair of the movement faculty of the Dr. Ida Rolf Institute® (formerly the Rolf Institute® of Structural Integration), Mary teaches workshops tailored to the needs and interests of various groups such as dancers; Pilates, yoga, and fitness instructors; massage therapists; and people who sit for a living. Her articles have appeared in numerous health and fitness magazines and she hosts a popular blog at www.healyourposture.com.

References

Bond, Mary. 2007. *The new rules of posture: How to sit, stand, and move in the modern world*. Rochester, Vermont: Healing Arts Press.

———. 2012. "Heal your posture." Available from https://healyourposture.com/videos.

———. 2018. *Your body mandala: Posture as a path to presence*. Maitland, FL: MCP Books.

Doidge, Norman. 2015. *The brain's way of healing*. New York, NY: Penguin Random House, 168.

Gracovetsky, Serge. 1988. *The spinal engine*. New York, NY: Springer-Verlag, 9-17.

Feldenkrais Guild® of North America. 2022. "Feldenkrais method." Available from http://www.feldenkrais.com (accessed January 7, 2022).

Start at the Front of Spine, Go to the Back Body

Find the Backbones, What a Journey!

By Pierpaola Volpones, Advanced Rolfing® Instructor, Rolf Movement® Instructor

Pierpaola Volpones

ABSTRACT *This article considers the spine metaphorically, embryologically, and as a location for chronic pain. Faculty member Pierpaola Volpones discusses the journey of learning about backs, doing Rolfing SI back work, and teaching others how to help vertebrae find their way home.*

In symbolic language, since ancient times, the spine is often depicted as a tree, in which the vital lymph flows, and connects the Earth with the sky: the breath of the spirit is embodied in the body, to create the path of life. It's very common to consider the spine as a sacred place, the yogi tradition teaches of kundalini and chakras, that they are positioned along the spine. The Kabbalah speaks of the tree of life with three pillars, the middle one being the reflection of the spine. For humans standing on two feet, the vertical spine is a metaphor for the evolution of our organism: this is what was stated by Ida P. Rolf, PhD.

The back is easily identified with strength and power; also, metaphorically speaking, it is the place to store things and to leave things. We want to get rid of elements that no longer serve us, we want to let go, and the spine is the designed place of the past: we walk forward facing the future, carrying the past at our back. Conversely, in some cultures the past is located in front of us, because we know it, we can

recall and see it, and the future is behind us, because we don't know yet what will happen. We humans sense the flow of life with our bodies, the timeline of existence is perceived with the front and the back of our bodies. In family systems therapy, our

Figure 1: Bust of the god Janus, Vatican Museum, Vatican City. Photo by Fubar Obfusco. This photo is in the public domain and can be found here, https://commons.wikimedia.org/w/index.php?curid=177247.

For humans standing on two feet, the vertical spine is a metaphor for the evolution of our organism: this is what was stated by Ida P. Rolf, PhD.

ancestors are behind us, supporting our backs. They are our roots.

Consider this: *"In ancient Roman religion and myth, Janus is the god of beginnings, transitions, gates, time, duality, doorways, passages and endings. He is usually depicted as having two faces, as the god can look at the future and the past"* (Wikipedia 2021, see Figure 1). Janus is divine . . .

As embryos, we develop from three tubes: the motor, the visceral, and the neural; the spine is the place of beginning of our differentiated development (see Figure 2). The shape of the spine continues to change from the moment we are born. Humans start in the primary kyphosis, over time we develop the cervical lordosis and the lumbar lordosis. This is driven by the vital instincts aimed at preserving life, the ones that push us to explore and to move into the world outside, looking for nourishment and pleasure. The dance of the curves of the spine is accompanied by the growth and development into verticality. We learn balance by falling, surrendering to gravity, and getting up; we become stronger and stronger in our muscles, refining their motor control.

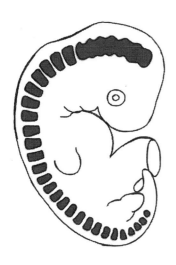

Figure 2: Primary c-curve of the embryo, the spine develops in this primary kyphosis.

Back and Back Pain

The spine and the vertebral column: these names describe the axial-complex characteristics of being pointed, peaked, spired, jagged, and layered. The spine speaks of the bones, the skeleton, and its bony collection of many pieces stacked on top of each other. I reflect on the meaning of 'column', that is to say that it's a column in the sense of a vertical, longitudinal organization, but not in the sense of being a weight-bearing structure, it is not like temple columns. We know that the human vertebral column is designed as a tensegrity structure where the load is transferred and distributed along its solid and tensile structures of muscles, fascia, ligaments, and tendons. Hidden within the word 'vertebral' is the action of moving toward, to orient toward as the Latin word *vertere* infers. Our spine is a set of piled-up little bones, designed to move, to *vertere*, to orient. The spine is designed to move, to carry, and to protect the spinal cord that is an extension of our brain into the body via the spinal canal. When the spine's motion and capacity is limited or restricted, we run into troubles: back pain.

Back pain is one of the most common issues that brings people to knock on our office door. They say, "I have back pain," and they might mean a number of different aches: lumbar, lumbosacral, sciatic, sacroiliac, and/or dorsal pain. Even shoulders and upper thoracic pain can be the region of their intense sensation – all these areas can lead a client to say they have *back pain.*

Because of this variety of presentations, I have learned that when a client arrives with back pain, I ask: "Show me with your hands where you have pain." And the gesture they do is useful information for my interventions. For example, if they move their fingers horizontally from right to left in the area of the base of the sacrum, it's most likely related to the sacrum. With this information, I will focus on checking mobility of the sacrum during the session, specifically the mobility of the sacrum with the iliac bones and the lumbar spine,

I will test the mobility of the coccyx, the resiliency of the sacrotuberous and sacrospinous ligaments. When they stroke their lumbar area, next to the spine, with the palm of the hand, most probably it is a low back pain. Does this mean that I concentrate on the lumbar spine? Not really. I have learned in years of practicing as a Rolfer® that lumbar pain can be related either to articular vertebral issues, or to happens below or above

> ## "Show me with your hands where you have pain." And the gesture they do is useful information for my interventions.

or in front of the lumbar spine. Among the 'below' possibilities there could be tissue restrictions, specifically a lack of continuity at pelvic floor, hips, hamstrings, knees, feet, and ankles. There are various regions of support from below that draw my attention to the lower limbs and the related diaphragms of a person with back pain. Among the 'above' possibilities I would include the thoracic spine, ribs, shoulders, and arms as areas of interest to consider tissue restrictions and misuse.

The space in front of the spine is occupied by fascial layers that are in close relationship with the visceral organs; think about the crura of the diaphragm that attach at the bodies of the lumbar vertebra and how the duodenum

Figure 3: Anterior view of esophagus entering the visceral space, stomach dissected away. Notice that the crura of the diaphragm is at the anterior aspect of the lumbar vertebrae and is continuous with suspensory ligament of the duodenum.

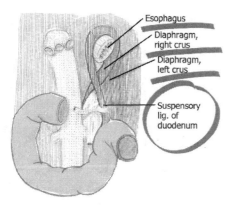

is connected to the diaphragm (see Figure 3). Notice the suspensory ligament of duodenum wrapping around the esophagus and melting with the crura of the diaphragm. Don't forget that the psoas shares the same space as the crura of the diaphragm, and is also attached at the lumbar spine. The different rhythms of breathing, walking, and digestion make the lumbar vertebrae reverberate in relationship to each other, and any out-of-tune functions may show up as *pain*.

Back Work in Rolfing SI

The back work of Rolfing Structural Integration (SI) practice has undergone various transformations. Traditionally by 'back work' we meant bench work, working the back in sitting. And even more traditionally, bench work was performed using both elbows stroking down the back while the client was slowly bending forward. When I was a new Rolfer, I remember doing Second-Hour bench work with a client who was a man in his sixties with lumbar pain, and this moment taught me a crystalline lesson that this kind of back work is not always a good strategy. The guy could not come back up from flexion – posterior lumbar vertebrae don't like positions that push them even more posterior. They don't like that at all, particularly if there is no support. You might be curious what I did with the client; in my shame and fear, I helped him to sit and to stand up, and I invited him to come back the next day for another session. Then I gave him a Third Hour that

saved his back, and my self-confidence! I *trusted the* Recipe. Looking at him, it was obvious to me that balancing the front and the back, with length and space along the lateral line, was a good solution for him. I used the tools I had at that time.

We have experimented with back work that could be done supine, from underneath; prone, therefore from above; sidelying; and sitting. All these positions help us to reach different goals and layers of the myofascial and articular system. We have learned to use hand and feet activation with seated work to free the spine, and we play with the support of the sit bones to impact the axial complex. The direction of the interventions is not always from top to bottom; in fact, in the lumbar area it is helpful to move upward instead of the traditional downward back work. It takes off some pressure at the lumbosacral junction, and it encourages a restoration of the natural lordosis, when that is part of the mobility that has been lost (see Figure 4).

Teaching Back Work

Teaching back work fascinates me particularly. Rolfing instructors spend little time teaching back work during the Basic Training. There is so much to do that back work occupies very few days within the eight weeks of Phase II or III. Even when we know that we don't chase

symptoms, being able to address back restrictions, either myofascial or articular, is an important tool to add to our toolbox that allows new Rolfers to meet their clients' needs and requests.

I have struggled to find a way to teach spinal mechanics. Even with the useful book *Spinal Manipulation Made Simple* (2001; see Figure 5) by Jeffrey Maitland, PhD, it's not simple to remember where the vertebra is fixed (open or close) and what to do accordingly. He writes, "Keep practicing this shotgun approach until you gain confidence with feeling rotation and releasing facet restrictions . . . you will learn how to apply the test so you don't waste time trying to release what is not restricted" (Maitland 2001, 25). He is also concerned that *we don't waste time* and that we find an easy and efficient execution of back work. Maitland and Michael Salveson were my teachers at my advanced Rolfing training; both were very dedicated in teaching us how to grasp vertebral-biomechanical tests and interventions. *Understanding* the biomechanics and *practical application* of the knowledge can each take their own time to acquire confidently. Ultimately, as Maitland writes, continuing to practice is a must.

Since there is so much for new Rolfers to acquire during Basic Training, and the back work is introduced in a limited amount of time, it is good advice for our new colleagues to keep learning

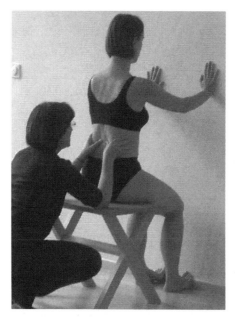

Figure 4: Pierpaola Volpones demonstrating back work with client.

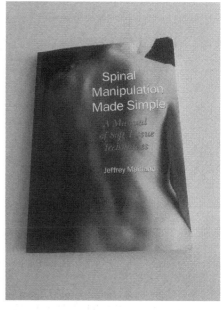

Figure 5: Jeffrey Maitland's 2001 book, *Spinal Manipulation Made Simple*.

Vertebrae, and bones in general, want to go back home; this is what my teachers used to say. Let's find the way home.

back work from Dr. Ida Rolf Institute® (DIRI) continuing education instructors. This is what I did as practitioner, before becoming a teacher. I attended several workshops to improve my skills. It is initially frustrating testing each vertebra's motion, trying to understand if it is fixed open or closed, then to remember where to work accordingly, but it is worth it in the end. I found it very cortical and brainy at first, of very little help in my practice.

So, I decided to take a different route. I studied back work with my clients, I taught myself by looking for mobility where I felt restrictions, I used direct and indirect touch, I followed the tissue and listened to the tissue, which led me to encouraging the vertebra to find its place. But teaching requires more precision. It worked in practice, but I had no theory to support my findings.

Then something I read about Fryette's laws of vertebral motion was a turning point that opened a new perspective for me. While there is agreement that Type I is universally true for all bodies, there is debate whether Type II applies to all backs, all the time. If I had only memorized these ideas and not trusted my touch and my training, I would have been stuck thinking about rules. The agreement for the Type I says, *sidebending of the thoracic and lumbar vertebrae is accompanied by a rotation toward the opposite side of the sidebend – when the vertebra has started the motion from neutral*. There is not common agreement about the Type II vertebral motion, *in flexion or extension (not in neutral), the vertebrae rotate and sidebend toward the same side*. Several authors disagree on this Type II law (Legaspi and Edmond 2007). Another glimmer of light was to learn that unilateral fixation is often due to visceral restrictions; only bilateral fixation is most probably due to articular issues. Thus, my choice to look for vertebral restrictions and finding ways to restore mobility was not so off track! This approach leaves me free to touch a specific place along the spine, listening to the tune the vertebra plays, and gives me time to start dancing

with the vertebra, following and leading, until the whole spine and the whole back become part of the entire organism. *Vertebrae, and bones in general, want to go back home*; this is what my teachers used to say. Let's find the way home.

Pierpaola Volpones discovered Rolfing SI through bodywork and her research into well-being and somatic expression. She studied in Munich with Stacey Mills and Michael Salveson in her Basic Training and with Michael Salveson and Jeffrey Maitland in her Advanced Training. Her Rolf Movement training took place in Italy with Janie French and Annie Duggan. She began her Rolfing SI and Rolf Movement teacher training almost twenty years ago, and she has been teaching since 2005. She runs a practice in Rimini, Italy, and teaches for the European Rolfing® Association. Her website is www.volpones.it.

References

Legaspi, Owen & Susan L. Edmond. 2007 Apr. Does the evidence support the existence of lumbar spine coupled motion? A critical review of the literature. *Journal of Orthopaedic and Sports Physical Therapy* 37(4):169-178.

Maitland, Jeffrey. 2001. *Spinal manipulation made simple*. Berkeley, CA: North Atlantic Books.

Wikipedia contributors, "Janus," *Wikipedia, The Free Encyclopedia,* https://en.wikipedia.org/w/index.php?title=Janus&oldid=1061064297 (accessed December 20, 2021).

Human Locomotion, Persistence Hunting, and Gracovetsky's Spinal Engine Theory

By Per Haaland, Basic Rolfing® Instructor and
Rolf Movement® Instructor

Per Haaland

ABSTRACT *Faculty member Per Haaland explores the role of the axial complex in human locomotion. Haaland discusses the importance of persistence hunting in human evolution and how Serge Gracovetsky's spinal engine theory posits the spine's centrality to human locomotion. Hubert Godard's tonic function model further describes the sophisticated interplay between tonic and phasic muscles in human locomotion. A deeper understanding of these theories and models will help our work in structural integration and movement education.*

Human beings have a distinct style of locomotion. We walk upright on two feet. Over the last decades, research and inquiry into the biomechanics of human gait have dramatically increased our understanding of human locomotion. Serge Gracovetsky, PhD, with his *spinal engine theory*, has been one of the most significant contributors to this inquiry (1988). Assessing the presence and expression of contralateral gait, a fundamental tenet of the spinal engine theory, is an important part of the training of structural integration (SI) practitioners. All manual therapists and somatic educators can benefit from a deepening of our understanding of the spinal engine model. In this paper, I aim to explain and expound on Gracovetsky's theory in a way that I hope to be useful for other SI practitioners and movement educators. I believe that deepening our understanding of the biomechanics of human gait can help us better understand what makes our work so effective in changing posture and improving coordination.

To begin understanding human gait, it is helpful to examine an important theory regarding our uniquely human style of locomotion.

Humans: Long Distance Persistence Hunters

It has been hypothesized that early humans, after having evolved bipedality, specialized as long-distance runners for their survival, practicing what has been termed *persistence hunting*. As explained by Christopher McDougall in his book *Born to Run*, this type of persistence hunting was, until recently, still being practiced among certain tribes in sub-Saharan Africa (2011). Upon encountering a herd of animals, say, antelopes, a band of humans would identify a weak member of the herd and then attempt to separate it from the rest of the animals. At that point several members of the group would start running after the animal. When the hunters had chased their prey for some time, the animal would eventually get exhausted and collapse, at which point the hunters would kill it. Thus, persistence hunting ensured an essential supply of animal protein and fat, satisfying our bodies' general nutritional needs as well as our expanding brain's need for fuel.

Features that Humans Evolved for Efficient Locomotion

What makes humans such exceptionally good long-distance runners?

Sweat Glands

An important factor in hominid evolutionary development had to do with temperature regulation. According to *Scientific American:* "The transition to naked skin and an eccrine-based sweating system . . . offset the greater heat loads that accompanied our predecessors' newly strenuous way of life" (Jablonski 2012, 23). Sweating allows for *efficient temperature regulation* as the sweat, perspiring onto the surfaces of the body, cools the skin. An antelope, like most other mammals, would regulate its body temperature (cool off) through intensified breathing. Compared to sweating, this is a much less efficient way of cooling the body. Inevitably, after some time running, the antelope would

collapse from overheating, at which point the hunters would kill the animal with little risk of injury to themselves.

Uncoupling the Breathing Rhythm from the Stride Pattern

Another important feature in hominid evolution was the capacity to *uncouple the breathing rhythm from the stride pattern*. For most animals there is one breath per stride. So, to run faster and farther requires animals to both breathe more heavily and attempt to cool themselves through panting. Humans, on the other hand, having uncoupled the breathing rhythm from the stride pattern, are able to regulate their breathing freely according to the moment-to-moment, ever-changing, need for oxygen.

Morphological Changes Related to Running

Comparing the dominant modes of locomotion in different mammals, McDougall references the work of Harvard paleoanthropologist Dan Lieberman, PhD, and Dennis Bramble, PhD, professor emeritus of biology who posits that, based on morphology, there are two main categories, *walkers* and *runners*.

Humans are categorized as runners. In contrast, chimpanzees, who are our closest primate relatives, are categorized as walkers. In chimpanzees the toes are long and splayed out, which means they are well suited for grasping and walking. In humans, the toes are short and stubby, a feature that suggests better efficiency for propulsion and running. Three other morphological features found in humans further support the *running human hypothesis* (McDougall 2011). The features linked to running as the main mode of locomotion are:

- The *nuchal ligament*.
- Well-developed *hip extensors (Gluteus maximus)*.
- The *Achilles tendon* and associated plantar flexion muscles.

The human cranium, weighing twelve to fifteen pounds, must be balanced on top

of the bipedal upright human frame. To balance and stabilize our large cranium, the long and powerful nuchal ligament developed in humans. Such a powerful stabilizing structure, spanning from the thoracic spine to the occiput, is not found in mammals whose gait is characterized by walking. Thus, the presence of the nuchal ligament suggests that early humans spent significant periods of time running.

Human bipedal locomotion relies on full hip extension, which requires large and powerful gluteal musculature. In contrast, in the case of the chimpanzee's facultative bipedality[1], the knees always remain bent, with their small gluteus maximus taking on the function of an abductor as opposed to a hip extensor.

The presence of the Achilles tendon and powerful plantar flexion muscles are other indicators that human beings are specialized for running. Chimpanzees, who are poor bipedal runners, lack an elastic tendon (the Achilles tendon) and instead have calf muscles that attach directly to the heel bone.

Gracovetsky, Controlled Instability, and the Spinal Engine Theory

The human locomotor system utilizes a phenomenon that has come to be known as *controlled instability*, a term coined by gait analyst Serge Gracovetsky (1988). Gracovetsky, a Canadian engineer, was led into the study of spinal functioning and the biomechanics of gait as a result of seeking help for a back problem. After having sought the counsel of seven different medical practitioners, he was given seven different explanations and seven different approaches for remedying his situation. He decided to do his own research and ended up proposing a new model for understanding human gait, the spinal engine theory. In his theory, Gracovetsky posits that human locomotion is characterized by what he calls controlled instability. He points to the fact that the unsupported spine will collapse under a mass of approximately

It has been hypothesized that early humans, after having evolved bipedality, specialized as long-distance runners for their survival, practicing what has been termed *persistence hunting*.

The human locomotor system utilizes a phenomenon that has come to be known as *controlled instability,* a term coined by gait analyst Serge Gracovetsky.

two kilograms. By virtue of this inherent instability, he says, the components and segments of the skeletal system are designed to be displaced easily, allowing for easy and smooth shape changes and moment-to-moment adjustments, such as flexion, extension, and rotation of the spine. This controlled instability offers our species evolutionary advantages.

What Drives Human Gait?

In Gracovetsky's 2001 paper "Analysis and Interpretation of Gait in Relation to Lumbo Pelvic Function," he addressed the question of what drives human gait. Before Gracovetsky's contribution to the debate, starting in the mid-1980s, the common view held by the gait analysis community was that the legs are the driving force in human locomotion. In this view, walking is simply a motion of the legs carrying its passive passenger, the trunk.

Countering this narrative, Gracovetsky points to the fact that to achieve human gait, the pelvis needs to rotate in the horizontal plane (the 'table' plane; see Figure 1).

If the force needed to rotate (torque) the pelvis originates in the legs, he says, then a counter-torque would be observed at the level of the feet, as required by the physical law related to the conservation of angular momentum. Force plate data indicates that very little torque is applied to the ground during walking. This suggests, argues Gracovetsky, that no torque is transmitted from the legs to the pelvis. What, then, is responsible for pelvic rotation in the horizontal plane?

Features of the Human Spine

The spine, says Gracovetsky, is a curved, flexible rod (Gracovetsky 2001). In such a structure, a lateral bend induces an axial torque. Translated into terms we use as manual therapists, lateral flexion of the spine toward the right, i.e., a *right sidebend*, induces a *left rotation* of the spine; a *left sidebend* induces a *right rotation* of the spine (see Figure 2).

This mechanism is referred to as *coupled motion*. As the spine sidebends to one side and rotates to the other, this motion is transmitted into the pelvis through the sacroiliac juncture. In this way, spinal

movement powers pelvic rotation in the horizontal plane. This is the 'engine' that fundamentally drives walking, according to Gracovetsky. The spinal engine theory predicts that an individual without legs would be able to 'walk' on their ischia by means of this coupled motion between spine and pelvis.

In an experiment conducted with a legless individual as a subject, kinematics and electromyography studies were both able to demonstrate that this individual's pattern of movement was strikingly similar to that seen in bipedal gait (see Figure 3). Having thus demonstrated that the driving force for human locomotion is the spine, Gracovetsky further explains the role of the legs and the upper extremities.

The Role of the Legs

While it has been demonstrated that human bipedal locomotion can be achieved without legs, efficient locomotion, especially at high velocity, is dependent on increasing the power available to the organism. Increasing power means increasing muscular mass. As the expansion of the spinal extensor muscles in humans is restricted by the contents of the abdominal cavity, the increase in muscle mass must be located outside the trunk, such as with the hip extensors. The power that gets generated and temporarily stored within the hip extensors, primarily the gluteus maximus, is returned to the spinal engine via the ligamentous structures surrounding the sacroiliac joint. The legs greatly amplify the power of locomotion generated by the spinal engine.

The Role of the Arms

As we noted earlier, human gait is characterized by near-zero torque at the foot/ground interface. To prevent the foot from transferring torque to the ground, the pelvic girdle and the shoulder girdle counter-rotate to conserve the angular momentum. We call this contralateral motion. From the rotating thorax, the ipsilateral shoulder extends and furthers this spiraling motion, transmitting it through to the arms. The arms, through their pendular action, extend and amplify this rotation/counter-rotation energy transfer system, originally initiated in the lumbopelvic area.

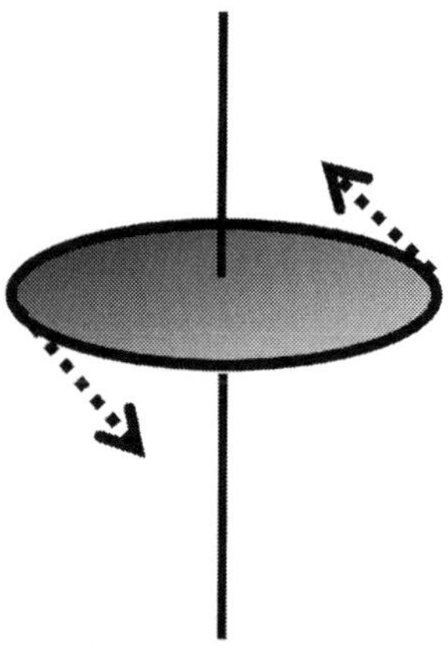

Figure 1: Axial rotation in the horizontal plane.

Left rotation

Right sidebend

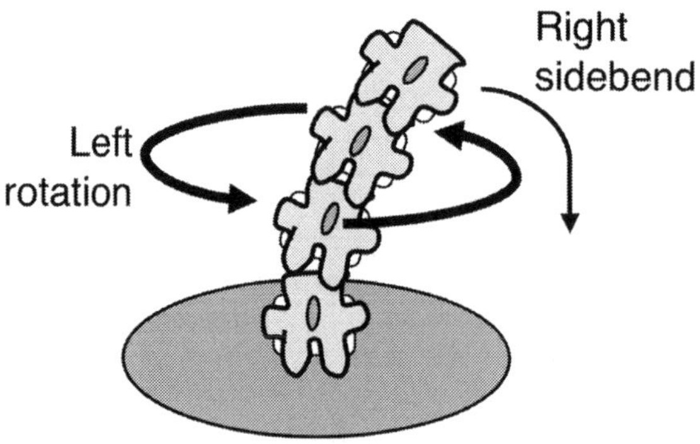

Figure 2: The spine is a curved, flexible rod. Motion is coupled, when the spine right sidebends, it is paired with left rotation.

Figure 3: Posterior view of the axial complex of a person sitting on a deck. Imagine this person walking their sit bones to the edge of the deck, they could do this by only moving their axial complex. Photo by Danie Franco on Unsplash.

Pathways of Muscle Power Transmission

As shown in Figure 1, for human contralateral gait to happen, the pelvis needs to rotate in the horizontal plane. Specific pathways of muscle power transmission ensure that this rotation/counter-rotation mechanism continues to propel our bodies forward in space.

During walking (and running), hip extensors fire as the toes push the ground. The muscle power thus generated is directly transmitted to the spine and trunk via two distinct but complementary pathways: the biceps femoris pathway (see Figure 4) and the gluteus maximus pathway (see Figure 5).

Chemical Energy Transformed from Kinetic to Potential and Back to Kinetic

When the toes of one foot push the ground, the hip extensors are triggered to fire. As a result of this muscular activation, the trunk is extended and raised (lifted up) in the sagittal plane. The chemical energy generated by the activated muscles is now converted – through the raising/lifting of the trunk – into potential energy which temporarily gets stored in the gravitational field. With the body mass thus elevated, the spine rearranges its geometry as the body readies itself to 'land' on the opposite foot. As the opposite foot lands, bringing the mass

of the body back toward the ground, the potential energy, temporarily stored in the gravity field, is liberated and becomes kinetic energy. This kinetic energy is then transformed and redirected as needed to initiate another cycle of rotation and counter-rotation of the upper girdle (rib cage/shoulders/arms) with respect to the lower girdle (pelvis and legs) and vice versa. In this way, energy continues to be efficiently exchanged and transferred between the different components of the locomotor system.

What is the relevance of persistence hunting ancestors and Gracovetsky's spinal engine model to our evolution as humans and to the practice of structural integration and somatic education?

The running human hypothesis offers an understanding of one of our early ancestors' survival adaptations. Our locomotor system is characterized by the capacity for long-distance persistence hunting. Important features of this capacity include: the development of sweat glands; uncoupling breathing from stride pattern; and morphological developments related to running. Gracovetsky's spinal engine theory explains how our unique bipedal locomotor system, by exploiting the laws of physics and kinetics, is primed to take advantage of properties such as inertia, momentum, and viscoelasticity. His theory shows how humans can efficiently recycle, redirect, and transform kinetic energy, minimizing the need for excess muscular effort. But what does this have

to do with our work as SI practitioners and somatic educators? And how can we help contemporary humans, often presenting with pain, movement restrictions, and less-than-optimal coordination patterns? How can we help our clients re-embody the elegant, energy efficient functional patterns of our ancestors?

Sensorimotor Amnesia

The average modern human can be said to have become afflicted by sensorimotor amnesia, a term coined by Thomas Hanna (2004) from his work with Moshe Feldenkrais. As infants and children, we explore our physicality with curiosity, joy, and excitement. We crawl, we roll, we twist, and we turn, flexing and extending as we curiously explore our environment. Infant movement exploration, from supine and prone through to quadrupedal, gradually helps the infant acquaint itself with its own spinal engine. Playing with sidebends and twists, we find joy in stretching and contracting, extending and flexing the muscles and fasciae surrounding the spine. The pride and mastery we feel as we take our first few steps upright is well earned. We slowly and painstakingly had to develop the coordination patterns, stabilization skills, and balancing capabilities that enabled us to master our own spinal engine.

Fast forward to school age, when our agile, flexible, and excitable bodies are forced into restrictive chairs and desks,

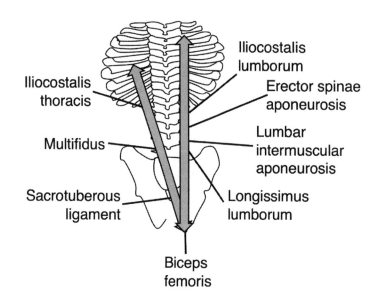

Pathway #1: Biceps femoris pathway

Figure 4: Biceps femoris pathway: Biceps femoris to sacrotuberous ligament to lumbar intermuscular aponeurosis (LIA). LIA is linked directly with the lumbar transverse processes via iliocostalis lumborum and longissimus lumborum and to spinous process vis multifidus (Gracovetsky 1988).

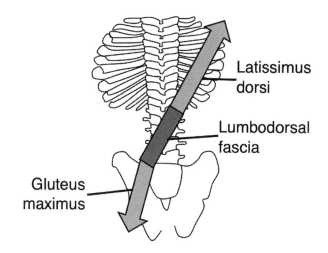

Pathway #2: Gluteus maximus pathway

Figure 5: Gluteus maximus pathway: Gluteus maximus to lumbodorsal fascia to latissimus dorsi to upper extremities (Gracovetsky 1988).

our frames expected to spend extended periods of time sitting still, bodies growing tense and restricted. As we grow into adults, further cultural and societal forces, such as gender stereotypes and fear of being sexually provocative, may make us subdued, minimizing freedom of movement, toning down the external appearance of pleasure and sensuality, to portray ourselves as responsible, well-adjusted adults. We become more cerebral, less embodied. We develop sensorimotor amnesia. Adult sensorimotor amnesia shows itself as a lack of adaptability, movement restriction, and lack of spontaneity. This diminishment of movement and flexibility results in inefficient coordination, greater wear on our joints, potential pain, and even tissue damage.

Reclaiming Our Birthright – Gravity, Evolution, and Human Potential

Observing the predicament of modern humans alienated from our own somatic awareness, Ida P. Rolf, PhD, offered structural integration as a means to further human potential through refining our relationship with gravity. The benefits of structural integration, as we know, include improved structure/posture, enhanced coordination, and a fuller sense of self-expression.

Hubert Godard: The Tonic Function Model

Hubert Godard, a French Rolfer®, Rolf Movement Practitioner, dancer, and faculty member for the European Rolfing® Association, has given us many tools to be able to apply what Rolf was pointing to. Godard has helped update the SI community regarding research in perception, coordination, and body mechanics. His contributions have improved our understanding of how and why structural integration is effective and therefore helping us help our clients achieve the benefits of our work. Godard's most important contribution may be the *tonic function model*. In the article "Tonic Function: A Gravity Response Model for Rolfing Structural and Movement Integration," written by Advanced Rolfer and Rolf Movement instructor Kevin Frank (1995), the main premises of Godard's model are laid out, including the model's

Gracovetsky's spinal engine theory explains how our unique bipedal locomotor system, by exploiting the laws of physics and kinetics, is primed to take advantage of properties such as inertia, momentum, and viscoelasticity.

relationship to Gracovetsky's spinal engine theory. Gracovetsky's 'controlled instability' (1988) is shown to offer humans evolutionary advantages and has important ramifications for us as body therapists. Human development, Frank notes, is closely linked to our relationship to gravity. He explains how we, as gravity-sensitive creatures, evolved structures and body systems specifically dedicated to ensure our capacity to balance and stay upright in the gravitational field.

Tonic Function: The Interplay Between Tonic and Phasic Muscles

Expounding on Godard's tonic function model, Frank explains how a body designed for instability can move quickly and efficiently by *letting go* (1995). We can change our position in space more quickly and efficiently when we let go, release and lengthen, as compared to initiating movement through muscle effort. For humans to manage and take advantage of this controlled instability, there have been parallel improvements in the complex body systems designed to assure our stability and uprightness in the gravitational field. These body systems are known collectively as our *gravity response system*. Humans' sophisticated gravity response system enables us to maintain upright balance and coordination without conscious control. Our controlled instability allows us to harness, convert, and redirect physical and kinetic forces with a minimum of energy expenditure. An important feature of this system is the subtle interplay between two types of muscles: *tonic muscles* and *phasic muscles*.

Tonic muscles (stabilizer muscles) are engaged in the continuous, moment-to-moment negotiations required to stay upright in the gravity field. These muscles have a way of metabolizing oxygen which gives them great endurance and allows them to be 'on' for long periods of time.

Phasic muscles are action muscles, muscles, they are responsible for our movements, actions, and gestures in the world. These muscles are designed for brief bursts of activation and are not meant to stay 'on' for long periods of time.

For the body to move efficiently and fluidly, an intricate orchestration takes place in which tonic muscles provide the underlying, subconscious stabilization needed for the phasic muscles to perform voluntary actions. Our *gravity response system* functions optimally when moment-to-moment stabilization is left to the muscles that are best suited for this purpose, the tonic muscles or stabilizers. Tonic muscle coordination creates the underlying stabilization needed to enable phasic muscles to freely move, act and express in the world.

Understanding the Significance of Tonic Function – Structural Integration and Somatic Education as Antidote to Sensorimotor Amnesia

When tonic and phasic muscles function together in a balanced and differentiated manner, good stabilization patterns are developed and sustained. Stabilization patterns can, however, become disorganized, sometimes leading to a dysfunctional situation where phasic muscles habitually take on the role of tonic muscles. Stabilizing the body in unnatural positions – such as when driving a car or sitting for long hours at a desk in front of a computer – may contribute to our shifting into unhealthy postures and suboptimal coordination patterns. Flattened lumbar curves, muscle tightness, and movement restrictions can ensue. "Our coordinative code has been corrupted, leading to a system-wide deterioration of function" (Frank 2014, 53).

In structural integration, we use fascial mobilization techniques, visualization, and guided movement to re-structure the body by talking to the "movement brain" (Frank 2014, 53). Frank suggests that our work in structural integration may be due in part to our capacity to affect coordinative change, as we facilitate "a system-wide restoring of stability" (Frank 2014, 55). By actively differentiating muscle groups, restoring and clarifying the differentiation between body parts (i.e., pelvis and thorax), we can help fine-tune the interplay between tonic and phasic muscles. By restoring the optimal balance between tonic and phasic muscle effort, we help restore healthy posture and graceful, efficient coordination. As we educate our clients through manual touch, movement prompts, and attention to sensation, we can help them optimize the efficiency of their spinal engine, evoking efficient contralateral gait.

The legacy from our persistence hunter ancestors is a high level of coordination and efficiency. Let's use our skill sets as structural integrators and movement educators to help our clients experience it.

Endnote

1. "Animals, including chimpanzees and gorillas, that assume bipedalism on a temporary basis in order to perform a particular function practice a form of locomotion called facultative bipedalism" (The University of Texas 2022).

Per Haaland is a Certified Advanced Rolfer, Rolfing Instructor, and Rolf Movement Instructor. Per received his Basic Rolfing Training in 1989 and completed his Advanced Training in 1994. Studies with Hubert Godard and Kevin Frank shaped his understanding of

SI as an interactive somatic education, highlighting perceptual and coordinative processes. Haaland's inclusive teaching style enables Rolfers to easily and confidently expand their SI skills into Rolf Movement applications. Per lives and practices in Santa Cruz, CA.

Per Haaland's next webinar class is "Embodying Rolf's Structural Integration Recipe" starting Sunday April 10th. Email Per for more information (perhaaland@ baymoon.com), details available at rolf.org, continuing education calendar.

References

Frank, Kevin. March 1995. Tonic function: A gravity response model for Rolfing structural and movement integration. *Rolf Lines* 23(1):12-20.

———. 2014. Structural integration psoas intervention considered in terms of normal stability response for hip and trunk flexion: A perceptive-coordinative view. *IASI Yearbook of Structural Integration:* 52-68.

Gracovetsky, Serge. 1988. *The spinal engine*. New York, NY: Springer-Verlag.

———. 2001. Analysis and Interpretation of Gait in Relation to Lumbopelvic Function. 4th Interdisciplinary World Congress on Low Back and Pelvic Pain, Montreal, Canada.

Hanna, Thomas. 2004. Somatics: *Reawakening the mind's control of movement, flexibility, and health*. Cambridge, MA: Da Capo Press.

Jablonski, Nina G. December 2012. The naked truth. *Scientific American* 22:22-29.

McDougall, Christopher. 2011. Born to run: *A hidden tribe, superathletes, and the greatest race the world has never seen*. New York, NY: Vintage Books.

The University of Texas, Department of Anthropology, eFossils Production Credits. "What is bipedalism?" Available from: http://efossils.org/book/what-bipedalism. Accessed January 15, 2022.

Assessment and Manual Intervention for the Psoas and Iliacus Muscles

By Jeffrey Burch, Certified Advanced Rolfer®

Jeffrey Burch

ABSTRACT *Jeffrey Burch presents a step-by-step approach to assess and then do manual interventions with the psoas and the iliacus. His concise and clear discussion, with an efficient technique, may change your elbow-in-the-abdomen method.*

Assessment of Psoas and Iliacus Muscles

This assessment protocol is for the two psoas major muscles and the two iliacus muscles, considered a functional group. There are other muscles that must be in balance with these four, including the lumbar and lower thoracic erector muscles, the respiratory diaphragm, the musculature of the pelvic floor, and the musculature of the abdominal wall (see Figure 1). The methods described here can be profitably adapted to these other muscles and muscle groups.

Any muscle can have:

1. An appropriate ability to lengthen or not,

2. a good ability to contract or not,

3. a resting length that can be hypotonic, just right, or hypertonic.

These three factors are at least partially independent of each other, and they can be separately assessed. Depending on the situation found, different strategies are required to move toward good balanced function.

Features of the status of a muscle can be assessed by gently contacting the muscle while monitoring it with finger contact. Then while staying in contact, ask for a sequence of actions:

1. Ask for voluntary contraction of that muscle.

2. Ask for movement which lengthens that muscle in a fashion that avoids eccentric contraction.

Self-Exploration

To experience this, place one of your arms on a table so the elbow can be flexed

Figure 1: Anterior view of the two psoas major muscles and the two iliacus muscles. Copyright Thieme Medical Publishers, Inc 2017.

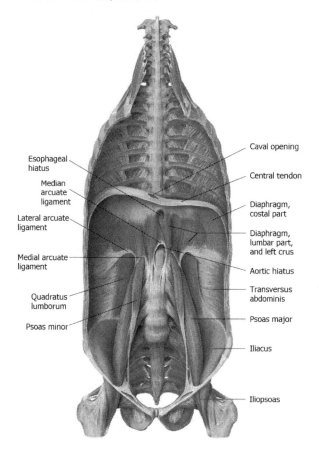

Esophageal hiatus

Median arcuate ligament

Lateral arcuate ligament

Medial arcuate ligament

Quadratus lumborum

Psoas minor

Caval opening

Central tendon

Diaphragm, costal part

Diaphragm, lumbar part, and left crus

Aortic hiatus

Transversus abdominis

Psoas major

Iliacus

Iliopsoas

and extended while the forearm glides on the tabletop. (This avoids working against gravity.) Start with the elbow fairly straight. Gently contact the biceps brachii muscle of that arm with the fingers of your other hand. Staying in contact with that muscle, slowly flex the elbow noting with your fingers the feeling of the muscle contracting. How active is the muscle? Then, slowly extend the elbow back to near-end range. How well is the muscle able to lengthen; does it lengthen smoothly and easily; or does it feel like a rubber band being stretched? Repeat this with the other arm. How do the two biceps compare? Next, assess in the same way the short head of the biceps brachii by contacting from the side, closer to the humerus.

Psoas and Iliacus Assessment

The psoas major and iliacus muscles participate in open kinetic chain hip flexion (that is to say, the leg is loose in space during flexion) and external rotation, particularly when the hip is flexed at least ninety degrees. At less than ninety degrees of hip flexion, these muscles often contract but have little power to move the femur. In a closed kinetic chain where the leg is fixed against the ground, contraction of the iliacus muscle anteriorly rotates that ilium, and contraction of the psoas major muscle deepens the lumbar curve. Start by having the client do the exercise described for the biceps brachii to familiarize them with the process. Invite them to experience the felt sense in the muscle during contraction and elongation under the mild pressure from your finger. You may also invite them to put their finger on the muscle during these motions. The felt sense through their fingers may assist them in recognizing the proprioceptive sense within the muscle.

For the psoas and iliacus, client movements described below may seem unfamiliar or odd. Have the client rehearse them a little before you make the assessment contacts.

To apply this to the psoas major and iliacus muscles, have the client lie on one side of the table. To assess the client's right psoas and iliacus, have the client's right side up. Start with the knees and hips comfortably flexed. Have a pillow under the client's head. Sit on a stool at the side of the table facing the client's abdomen. As support, put your left hand on the right iliac crest and just superior to it with the fingertips resting around to the client's back. With the tips of your right fingers, contact the abdominal wall in a sagittal line just lateral to the right lateral border of the rectus abdominus. The center of your contact is best at about the umbilical level. Slowly sink your fingers in until you encounter something firm at the depth of the back of the abdominal cavity. This should be easy. If you encounter great stiffness on the way in, there may be abdominal adhesions. If so, do not persist with this. Other work needs to be done before you can test the psoas.

Assuming you can contact the psoas,

1. First, move your fingertips a little lateral and then medial to feel the width and bulk of the psoas muscle. Remember the felt sense of this.

2. Next, ask the client to slowly extend both the right knee and hip together *without* lifting the right leg from the left leg. Let it slide. As the client does this, feel the extent and fashion in which the psoas major muscle elongates. Does it easily elongate? Or is there a feeling of elastic stretch - like the stretching of a rubber band? Remember your observations.

Start by having the client do the exercise described for the biceps brachii to familiarize them with the process.

Instruct the client to extend the hip and knee, at the same time, to think of this muscle melting and pouring down through the groin area and into the medial aspect of the thigh (adductor compartment).

3. Once the right leg is extended in line with the torso, ask the client to stop and let the leg momentarily rest.

4. Next, ask the client to slowly flex the right knee and hip, bringing the knee forward and up – again without lifting the leg. As the client does this, feel with your fingers for the contraction of the psoas major. How active is it? How strong does the muscle feel? Remember these observations.

5. Ask the client to deepen the lumbar curve a little by arching their low back toward you. You may need to shift your left hand to the lumbar spine to guide this movement which will be unfamiliar to many clients. Next ask the client to flatten their lumbar spine minimizing the participation of the abdominal wall. This asks for contraction of the shorter fibers of the psoas running from vertebra to vertebra. Remember what you feel.

Now change your right-hand contact to the right iliacus muscle. To accomplish this, withdraw your hand from the abdomen. Move your finger contact inferolateral from the psoas contact point, to the anterior and slightly medial part of the right ilium and with your hand palm up. Sink gently in, then move your fingertips lateral to contact the body of the right iliacus muscle. Note the bulk of the muscle. Now ask the client to make the same sequence of movements as you recently did for the psoas,

1. Ask the client to slowly extend both the right knee and hip together *without* lifting the right leg from the left

leg; let it slide. As the client does this, feel the extent and fashion in which the iliacus muscle elongates. Does the iliacus muscle elongate easily or does it feel like a tight rubber band? Remember this.

2. Once the right leg is extended in line with the torso, ask the client to stop and let the leg momentarily rest.

3. Next, ask the client to slowly flex the right knee and hip, bringing the knee up. As the client does this, feel with your fingers for the contraction of the iliacus muscle. How active is the iliacus? How strong does the muscular contraction feel? Remember this as well.

Break contact with both hands. Ask the client to roll over onto the other side and make notes of your findings. Walk around to the other side of the table to again sit facing the client's abdomen. Perform the mirror image of the same tests for the left psoas major and iliacus muscles.

Psoas and Iliacus Manual Interventions

You now have data about the bulk, ability to contract, and ability to lengthen of each of these four muscles. Consider what changes in function are desirable to move this group toward balance.

A. If a muscle has low bulk and/or does not contract well,

1. Start with the client in a side-lying position with the side of the muscle of interest up.

2. Contact the muscle of interest with your fingers as before.

3. Have the client extend the leg.

4. Instruct the client to bring the knee forward, as the client flexes the hip, say, "Attempt to 'reel in' the leg using the muscle I am touching." Encourage the client to avoid using the abdominal wall musculature. From what you feel, give the client ongoing feedback about muscle performance. Typically, the ability to contract the muscle will initially be hit and miss. With a few cycles of bringing the leg down and then up, it will usually be notably improved. Be satisfied with modest gains. One thing to recognize is that a very weak muscle may fatigue after as little as one rep and become unresponsive. Don't push it.

5. For the short fibers of the psoas that flatten the lumbar curve, work with having the client flatten the lumbar curve using the psoas. Give feedback from your finger contact.

B. If a muscle does not lengthen well,

1. Start with the client in the familiar side-lying position with the side of interest up.

2. Contact the muscle with your fingers as before.

3. Instruct the client to extend the hip and knee, at the same time, to think of this muscle melting and pouring down through the groin area and into the medial aspect of the thigh (adductor compartment). Give the client ongoing feedback on the success in relaxing this muscle. Invite the client to feel the melting, lengthening from the inside.

4. If the above steps do not allow the muscle to lengthen, there may be a tight nerve to this muscle, which is making the muscle appear tight. To investigate this possibility:

Instruct the client to bring the knee forward, as the client flexes the hip, say, "Attempt to 'reel in' the leg using the muscle I am touching."

a. The innervation of the psoas is from the lumbar plexus at the levels of L1 to L3. The innervation of the iliacus is L2 to L4. To investigate tension in the nerve to the right psoas, ask the client to lie on the left side with the right side up, hip and knee moderately flexed.

b. Sit facing the client's abdomen. Place the left fingertips on the spinous processes of T12 to L4. Place the fingers of the right hand on the belly of the right psoas major muscle. Ask the client to begin extending the hip and knee. Do the spinous processes of any of the vertebra(e) L1 to L3 rotate to the right more or sooner than their neighbors? If so, the nerve root from this spinal level or levels is tight.

c. Ask the client to flex the hip and knee again and let the leg rest briefly. Change your contact on the vertebra from monitoring to controlling. Ask the client to start slowly extending the hip and knee again. When a first barrier engagement is felt at the vertebra(e), ask the client to pause the movement of the leg and relax.

d. You now have a first barrier stretch established on this nerve. As you feel release, ask the client to extend the right hip slightly more until the first-barrier is re-engaged. Ask the client to rest the leg here.

e. Work through a series of these first-barrier stretches. Ask the client to flex the hip again and retest the span of the nerve as above.

f. Use a similar process for the iliacus muscle but with your contact a little more inferior on the spine.

g. If the nerve is not releasing well with this process, your stretch may be greater than first barrier. Have the client flex the hip somewhat more and rest there momentarily. Then have the client begin to extend the hip very slowly as you feel for the first hint of pull. A useful instruction for the client could be to extend the hip at a speed like 'grass growing'.

Additional Consideration: Inguinal Canal

In an untreated body, a very common limitation in both iliopsoas groups is reduced glide through the inguinal canal. Before engaging in the above assessment and manual interventions, it is profitable to assess the glide of the Iliopsoas group through the inguinal canal. This can be done with the client supine.

For the right leg, stand at the client's right side facing the thigh. Place your right hand under the client's knee. With your left hand, locate the inguinal ligament. Stabilize the inguinal ligament. Then, with your right hand at a moderate pace, flex and externally rotate the hip by lifting the knee while allowing external rotation at the hip. As you do this, monitor the sensation at the inguinal ligament. Does the iliopsoas group easily glide superior under the inguinal ligament or not?

Instruct the client to relax and not to help as you move their leg. Continuing to monitor the inguinal ligament, use your right hand to extend the hip, internally rotate it, and later in the movement, abduct it. This combined motion requires lengthening of the iliopsoas group by using the femur to pull on the iliopsoas. As you make this motion, does the iliopsoas easily glide under the inguinal ligament or not? Note how far the leg will move at the hip joint in this combined motion direction.

If the iliopsoas does not glide freely through the inguinal canal, it can be freed in any of several ways. Here is one. While monitoring the stabilized inguinal ligament, move the leg slowly through the range described – from extension-external rotation with abduction to flexion-internal rotation. As you move through this range, find the position of greatest ease where the iliopsoas drags the least on the inguinal ligament and on the pubic bone deep to it.

When you are very slowly moving the leg toward a little greater extension-internal rotation-abduction, notice when the first hint of a pull is felt at the inguinal ligament. Pause at this first barrier; wait for a sense of release. The felt release may range from slight to great. As the release is felt, slowly move the leg slightly further into extension-internal rotation-abduction until a new first barrier is felt. Pause there for a release.

Continue this process through a succession of releases. If at any barrier a release is not felt, slightly slack the tension induced from the femur. The position held may have been more than first barrier. Once several releases have been experienced, reassess the glide as before to see how much you have released it. If the release is incomplete, resume manual interventions starting with finding what is now the new place of greatest ease.

From all the suggestions listed here, make notes of everything you observed and did. Reassess at the next session with that client by referring to your notes to see what change had occurred in the interval between sessions. Continue these manual interventions as needed.

Jeffrey Burch received bachelor's degrees in biology and psychology, and a master's degree in counseling from the University of Oregon. He was certified as a Rolfer in 1977 and completed his advanced Rolfing® Structural Integration certification in 1990. Jeffrey studied cranial manipulation in three different schools, including with French osteopath Alain Gehin. Starting in 1998, he began studying visceral manipulation with Jean-Piere Barral, DO, and his associates, completing the apprenticeship to teach visceral manipulation. Although no longer associated with the Barral Institute, Burch has Barral's permission to teach visceral manipulation. Having learned assessment and treatment methods in several osteopathically derived schools, he developed several new assessment and treatment methods that he now teaches, along with established methods. In recent years, he has developed original methods for assessing and releasing fibrosities in joint capsules, bursas, and tendon sheathes. He is also beginning to teach these new methods. Burch, as the founding editor of the IASI Yearbook, regularly contributes to it, as well as to other journals. For more information visit www.jeffreyburch.com.

Unlocking Facets with a Structural Algorithm

An Interview with John deMahy

by Lina Amy Hack, Certified Advanced Rolfer®, and John deMahy, RN, DOMPT, Certified Advanced Rolfer

Lina Amy Hack

John deMahy

ABSTRACT *In this interview, Lina Amy Hack asks John deMahy about his axial complex model. He teaches this in his structural algorithm continuing education courses for manual therapists, which give clear steps of spine evaluation and interventions.*

Lina Amy Hack: Hello, how are you and where do we find you today?

John deMahy: I'm good and sitting in my office in New Orleans.

LAH: Thank you for meeting with me and working with our Dr. Ida Rolf Institute® journal again. As we were preparing for our axial complex theme, you came to mind because of your expertise with axial work, specifically your spinal algorithm system. What are your techniques based on?

JdM: First let's look at one of the foundational concepts of structural algorithms. That is, movement restrictions in the joints of the axial skeleton cause changes throughout our client's structure. Among these are changes in gait, leg length, pelvic inclination, and spinal curvature. A client will exhibit these changes long before the fascial changes occur. Attempting to address these fascially can waste an incredible amount of time. Possibly leaving our client in pain. The structural algorithms are designed to expedite the location and treatment of the restrictions. Then we can get on with our job of integrating their structure. As for intervention, the primary technique I use for treatment is muscle energy technique.

LAH: Let's start there, what does muscle energy technique mean?

When a facet locks or rib locks, becomes movement-restricted, it's your body actually working the way it was designed. There's nothing wrong. The body is doing what it is supposed to do because it's protecting you from something much worse.

JdM: In the axial skeleton, there are protective reflexes in all of the facets and the costal joints, the costovertebral joints, and the pelvis with the iliosacral joints. Each of these joints has a functional range of motion. If they go beyond that functional range, there's a protective reflex that locks it down. There are a lot of theories about the physiological cause. There have been lots of academic arguments about who is right.

This is the way I describe the technique to my clients. When the joint goes past its functional range, a protective reflex is engaged. This keeps the joint from causing greater damage to the tissue around it. When a facet locks or rib locks, becomes movement-restricted, it's your body actually working the way it was designed. There's nothing wrong. The body is doing what it is supposed to do because it's protecting you from something much worse. Protective reflexes responsible for locking the axial joints are actually doing their job. And this is the way I see the muscle energy technique. If you read the work by Fred Mitchell, DO, FAAO, or Philip E. Greenman, DO, FAAO, they don't describe it quite that way, but this is much easier to understand.

So how do we release the movement restriction? We put the body into a position where the joint is right up on the protective reflex without engaging it. Then we stimulate a different reflex that overrides the protective reflex. This gives us a couple of seconds to move the joint back into its functional range. Once in its functional range, the protective reflex is no longer being stimulated. Functional movement is restored. Now, movement is free because protection is no longer necessary. Does that make sense?

LAH: That's a great description.

JdM: It's such an important thing for people to understand. We often think our bodies are broken when we have pain, often they are not.

LAH: Right, clients will believe that their body has failed them somehow when they feel pain, yet it can be a protective response. It is important to teach this to people.

JdM: Just this morning I had a client who was upset about how much her body hurt when she gets out of her car. When she's in a meeting, her back starts to hurt. I said, "Fantastic. You know your back is telling you to be careful when sitting for prolonged periods of time, to be careful when getting out of your car." The pain is showing where to be careful in your life.

LAH: That's so smart. As a Rolfer, when I have people present having been cleared medically yet still suffer back pain, I think to myself there is going to be a lot of good stuff happening here for them.

JdM: Yeah, when people tell me that, I go, "Oh you are going to like this."

LAH: I'm very curious to learn how you think when someone presents with the confirmed bulging discs or the confirmed pinched nerve, the confirmed spondylosis. What is your process to help them?

JdM: Fine, I think, all aboard. The only contraindication I have is if the person is in so much pain I cannot put them in positions in which I need to have them in. If that happens, I'll stop a session and recommend they go see their doctor. This so rarely happens because they probably wouldn't get to my office in the first place if the pain is that severe.

LAH: Do you ever work with a client who wants you to collaborate with their physician?

JdM: The medical community is just beginning to open up in New Orleans. If they have heard of Rolfing® Structural Integration (SI), most would think it was like getting a rub down at the gym. I did have a gastroenterologist, with back pain, come to see me as a client. His father-in-law dragged him in, because he was tired of hearing him complain. This client was out of pain in about ten minutes. Then a month later, one of his patients came to see me and I asked, "Could you tell me what your doctor said that I do here?" The guy got kind of embarrassed. He said, "You do something like voodoo, but you don't kill any chickens."

LAH: Funny, Rolfing SI can seem like magic to people who don't know that we are studied professionals.

JdM: Yeah, we know exactly what we're doing. I've probably had about ten to fifteen physicians in my office and none of them can figure out what I'm doing. But the thing is they are doctors of medicine and pharmaceuticals, and that is not how this works.

LAH: My sister is a physician and when I was becoming a Rolfer, she was studying medicine. One day I said to her, "What's it like studying health and wellness?" She said, "I don't study health and wellness, I study disease."

JdM: Yes, exactly.

LAH: Tell me, how long does it take to do your structural algorithm? Is it something that you do for a whole session?

JdM: No, the algorithms are there to expedite a session not replace it. Let me give an example, the lumbar/pelvic algorithm. If somebody comes in with low back pain, hip pain, or any difficulty in the lower extremity, I'll start with the lumbar/pelvic algorithm.

Let me share a piece of the lumbar/pelvic algorithm, this is the sacral section (see Figure 1). It's like a flow chart, there's another section before this part, and there's a section after this as well.

LAH: Right, that makes sense, you have a progression of decisions to guide the practitioner. Kind of yes/no questions that lead to specific interventions.

JdM: Exactly, if one test is negative, no action is needed and you go to the next test. If that test is negative, you keep going down the line. That's the way an algorithm works.

To get to this section you would have already addressed the pubic symphysis, upslip, and lumbar restrictions. To get

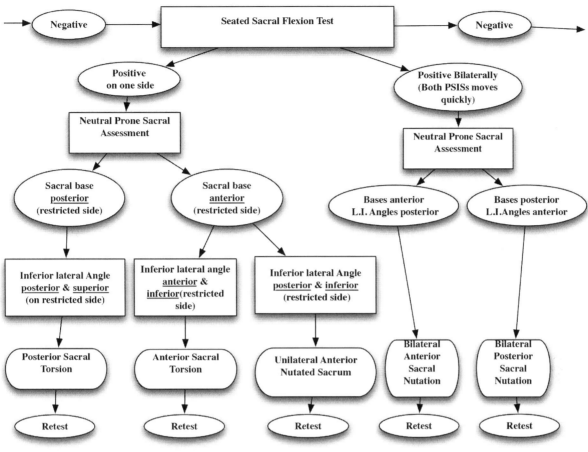

Figure 1: Sacral section of deMahy's structural algorithm.

John deMahy ©2012

to this part of the algorithm everything preceding is functional. Now, looking at the chart, we do the seated sacral flexion test. If it's positive on one side, you come down to the bubble, which is the prone sacral assessment. The prone sacral assessment is basically palpating the sacral assessing for rotations. If the sacral base is posterior on the restricted side, and the inferior angle is posterior and superior, then you have a posterior sacral torsion. You also get directed to the page number of the procedure in the manual (see Figure 2). It provides a picture of the procedure and the step-by-step guide on how to do it. I also provide a laminated chart that practitioners can put on the wall of their office to use while learning the system.

LAH: Nice, very logical flow, easy to follow.

JdM: The workbook is set up with clear photographs so hopefully people say, "Oh, I remember him doing that. Oh, I've done this before."

LAH: You sound like a practical thinker. What inspired you to create this model?

JdM: I did this for myself. There was a hole in my practice. People kept coming in with problems that I couldn't resolve. I felt like something was missing. I remembered the first lecture in school, Jan Sultan said that Dr. Rolf told them that it was their job to stand on her shoulders to continue advancing. Now it was going to be our job to stand on his shoulders. I started looking for something to fill the gap in my knowledge. Jan and Michael Salveson introduced spinal mechanics in my advanced class, so that's where I started. My research brought me to muscle energy technique. I started teaching it to myself. When I tried to teach it to another Rolfer, he said, "Listen, John, I don't have time to do all of this." He was right, just to do the testing to start took about an hour, even if you already have the tests memorized. When people are paying for a session with insurance, they don't mind an hour of testing. But when

people are paying out of their pocket, no, that doesn't work.

LAH: That's right.

JdM: Muscle energy technique is not our job. We want to get this done efficiently and quickly, so we can get on with integrating structure. And so I developed the structural algorithm to be able to move through assessment quickly. Instead of doing ten tests that are redundant, I found a sequence of tests where the practitioner can say to themselves, "Okay, this is it. If you do this test, this is the result. I don't have to do six more tests. This one tells me what I need to know. Let's do it and let's move on. Let's do the proper intervention, and move on." That's when the algorithm came in.

Algorithms have been used in healthcare for decades. They are to expedite the assessment and deliver the proper treatment as fast as possible. So, what I wanted to do as a Rolfer was to get all this information from muscle energy

Posterior Sacral Torsion

Observations on Restricted Side

• Seated flexion test:	Positive
• Sacral base:	Posterior
• Inferior Lateral angle	Posterior and superior
• Leg length:	Short

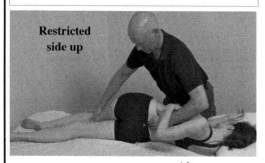

Restricted side up

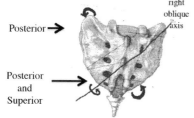

Posterior →

right oblique axis

Posterior and Superior →

Sacrum rotates Left on the Right oblique axis

Strategy:
Rotate L5 toward the sacral torsion to stimulate sacral rotation in the opposite direction. Use external femoral rotation to gap SI joint.

Client Position: Side-lying, restricted side up

Find extension barrier

1. Gently pull lumbars forward into slight extension.
2. Use the hand toward the client's head to monitor L5.
3. With the other hand, move the legs posterior. Stop at the point of movement of L5.
4. Change hands and monitor the sacral base with one hand, while using the other hand to reach under the shoulder and move the trunk posterior, stopping at the point of movement of the sacral base.

Find rotation barrier

5. Have client place hand of upper arm on waist. Place your hand between the arm and trunk and your elbow on client's shoulder.
6. While monitoring the sacrum, rotate the trunk by moving the upper shoulder posterior, stopping at point of movement of the sacrum.
7. Move the top leg anterior until the foot and knee rest on the table.

Client Action: Keeping the foot in contact with the table, press the knee toward the ceiling.

Continue with Procedural Outline page 3, #s 6 -7

Figure 2: Sample page from structural algorithm manual, the posterior sacral torsion page.

technique for the axial skeleton and distill down the essentials. I looked at what I would need to do that was essential to get results and move on. If somebody comes in and they have back pain or leg pain or something, then I say to myself, "Let's do the algorithm," and if all of the tests are negative, it's only been five minutes to find that out. In that case, then I would know it's all fascial rather than joint fixations.

But if I did find a joint restriction, then I'm saving an incredible amount of time. I could have wasted an entire five sessions being haunted by a lumbar facet or sacral restriction. We've all had the experience of working on somebody's back and it gets worse, that's what is happening when we fall into that hole. You might find yourself with your elbow pushing a joint back into place. The problem is you are pushing against a protective reflex, which is now going to push back even harder.

Often the client has two or three things that are going on, these kinds of things happen together, like sacral restriction and an L5 restriction often go together.

Once you know the algorithm, it takes ten to twenty minutes to know exactly what the client has going on, and you've saved yourself an incredible amount of time.

LAH: I would imagine our colleagues that have studied with you would also have more refinement in their ability to see these things as well. Seeing these details is a foundation of our work, which is very difficult. What you're offering is this practical, concrete, reproducible procedure.

JdM: One of the things about starting the session off with the algorithm is getting joint assessments out of the way. When somebody walks into your office and they've got joint restrictions in the axial skeleton, we have people stand up in front of us, we have them walk, and we're looking at their patterns, but we're not seeing their primary pattern. What we're seeing is the compensation for the joint restrictions and we see all of these compensations. It can fool us into thinking what you're seeing is the primary pattern that built up, and yet this is all temporary. Once you take all of those protective

mechanisms out, a lot of those patterns just drop away and their whole posture can change. Then we're seeing what our real job is, does that make sense?

LAH: Yes, it totally does.

JdM: The way I look at it is that the fascia is where we as Rolfers dance. But when there's glass on the dance floor, it's much better to sweep the glass up first and then dance. Joint restrictions are the broken glass. Rather than dance around, hopping around the glass so that you don't get your feet cut, sweep that away first.

LAH: You're painting a picture of that moment that I think every Rolfer knows where they invite the client off the table at the end of a session, your time is up, and then now you see the real pattern. The structural algorithm gets the practitioner there quicker, so useful.

With regard to the axial complex in general, do you think the weight of the body is mostly going through the spine? Or in your concept is body weight also going through the viscera, the myofascial, the adipose layers? When

The way I look at it is that the fascia is where we as Rolfers dance. But when there's glass on the dance floor, it's much better to sweep the glass up first and then dance. Joint restrictions are the broken glass. Rather than dance around, hopping around the glass so that you don't get your feet cut, sweep that away first.

I hear chiropractors speak, it leaves me with the impression that they seem to think that weight is only held by the spine. Our Rolfing SI concept is more dynamic, but it's not explained in a concrete way. Where is the weight transmission going with the axial spaces?

JdM: There is weight transmission throughout the body, not just the spine. That's one of the disadvantages of having a profession that's focused on one organ or on one segment of the body. Honestly, we have the same problem as we look at everything through our structural integration eyes focusing on fascia. It took me a while to wrap my mind around studying joints as hard as I did because it was like, "Well, Rolfing work is about fascia and we're supposed to be working with fascia." Medical doctors have the same thing, it's just what happens when you focus on one realm, you tend to not see the other stuff.

LAH: Yes, I've been working to reconcile reading the anatomy about the spine and the global view we take in structural integration. Spine texts lead me to think, wait, our spinal disks are not the only place bearing weight.

JdM: Not at all. That's the thing, the spinal disk is bearing weight, of course, but like a bulge or a herniation is a relationship of the amount of pressure coming on the disk and the integrity of the disk wall, that's the relationship we focus on. Yet, if everything just came through the spine, why is it that when we organize the core to strengthen it, it decompresses the spine? It wouldn't make sense if the weight only came through the spine.

LAH: Exactly, I've been wrestling with this idea, you're right, this is about the lens of the person writing the anatomy text compared to our wholistic concept. You mentioned to me earlier you've been developing new techniques around the rib algorithm, can you tell us more about that?

JdM: Yes, the ribs are very difficult to mobilize. Even the muscle energy techniques that I learned; the success ratio was not so good. I've been looking at how to find new techniques for ribs. Something I teach in my classes is that once you realize that it is just turning off protective reflexes, you can devise your own techniques. All you have to do is go to the edge of the protection reflex and turn it off.

Honestly, I learned the rib techniques in a dream. It was about a Rolfing class and I watched the teacher do this technique for the person's rib. I woke up and went, "Wow, that was a wild dream. This is so weird." Weeks later, I had a client with rib restrictions and nothing was working. I remembered the dream and tried it. It worked – once. Then it stopped working. But I knew I was on to something.

Over probably about five years of studying, asking myself, "How is it working? How about if I do it this way? How about if I do it that way? Oh, this one worked. What did I do this time that I didn't do last time?" I have refined the technique down to a high success rate and have it down to the point where it's almost no effort.

LAH: You're speaking on an important part of Rolfing SI where we do create unique interventions for each client. You've been systematic about it and it sounds like you have really good observation about yourself as a practitioner, especially in those creative moments.

JdM: Exactly. We have a job where we get to solve puzzles. People bring these puzzles to us every day. We solve them and then they give us money. What a wonderful job.

LAH: I agree. That's a great way to say it. We also work on our own puzzle of our own body while we're doing the work with our client's body. That's what I also love is

that we have to be in our own system, we have to understand our own physiology in order to be good at this job, our own health is served by doing the work.

Do you consider the ribs as part of the axial complex?

JdM: The ribs are anatomically part of the axial complex.

LAH: Other colleagues of ours think ribs are more of a sleeve structure. It's an interesting point to gather different points of view.

JdM: As far as the skeleton goes, it's axial. The extremities start at the collarbones and the sacroiliac joints. The concept of the sleeve is a metaphor that we use in structural integration for organization. For my purposes, the joints of the axial skeleton have those protective reflexes that we spoke of. The appendicular joints don't. The costovertebral joints have the protective reflex.

LAH: That is instructive. You were mentioning that you have client education that has become more developed over time. How do you specifically educate clients about their axial complex?

JdM: Like I mentioned, for people with back discomfort, I explain how the joints of the spine work. I explain about the protective reflexes and why they have them. That their body is not broken, it's doing the right thing. If they have a bulging disk or a herniation, I explain what it is. I have a model of the spine and I show them what happens. They have too much compression on that disk and the integrity of the disk wall is not strong enough. I get them engaged in the process. We have to mobilize the joints using the reflexes. Then with fascial work, get support coming up from the legs to give them support then decompression. Once this is done, then the scar can form around the disk.

I teach [clients] to think about their movements before they get themselves into trouble. For example, I might say to a client, "You have something you want in the back seat of your car. So, you reach back to grab it," and I demonstrate. Then I say, "In that move, you're arching back, rotating, and sidebending. For the facets on the right side of your spine, that is close (extension), close (side bending), close (rotation). What are the chances of you hitting that barrier where the protective reflex is going to kick in? It's pretty high."

In doing patient education I have begun to look at things differently and I changed the way that I teach our colleagues. As you're probably aware, spinal mechanics are incredibly complicated and difficult to learn. I found over the last fifteen years explaining to my clients what's going on in their backs, I realized that part doesn't have to be that complicated. Studying spinal mechanics is fascinating but you don't really need to know every single detail to start helping people. You don't have to memorize all of the terminology.

Starting with the basics can be the information that clients need – when you flex the facets open, when you extend the facets close. When you sidebend, one side opens and the other side closes. When you rotate, one side opens and one side closes. It's all about opening and closing.

Then I apply it to their lives. I teach them to think about their movements before they get themselves into trouble. For example, I might say to a client, "You have something you want in the back seat of your car. So, you reach back to grab it," and I demonstrate. Then I say, "In that move, you're arching back, rotating, and sidebending. For the facets on the right side of your spine, that is close (extension), close (sidebending), close (rotation). What are the chances of you hitting that barrier where the protective reflex is going to kick in? It's pretty high." I teach people that with each dimension that they go in, the chances are higher of getting restricted. That's a layperson's definition and application of Fryette's Laws. Makes much more sense when simplified that way.

I go through things they do every day. I suggest that while they are having back problems, they could think about moving their spine in one dimension at a time. They must pay attention while they have the pain. It is teaching them. If they are going to do something in more than one dimension at one time, they better have a strong core to be able to handle it. If they do engage their core strength, they can get away with it. For those clients with vulnerable backs, they're not going to get away with it. They are going to be back in our office with pain complaints.

LAH: That's nice, I like that. As a mom with kids in the back seat, that is a move I do all the time. Really great to remind a person about the safe way to do that gesture.

JdM: As an explanation, reaching into the backseat, if you reach too far the protective reflex kicks in, and one or a few facets may become locked in a closed position. But there is no pain at that time. Later when to bend forward to pick something up, the facets won't open, all the muscles contract, there's pressure on your disk, irritation on the nerves, and you would have back pain. Now you'd be walking with a new restricted pattern because you didn't want to straighten up because that's going to hurt.

LAH: Nice explanation, the full circle teaching of axial function. Like the person who reaches into their back seat then later does a left side shoulder check, getting a terrible *zing* in the neck.

JdM: Exactly, yes.

LAH: That's great, this is what our clients want. They need practical information that relates to how their bodies are living in their spaces – home, car, and so on.

For our readers that are not familiar with your continuing education (CE) classes, can you tell us a little bit about how you organize your courses?

JdM: The first thing I do in the class is help people switch from palpating soft tissue to palpating bones. In general, structural integrators train themselves so much to feel the layers and the details of the fascia, that when they go to palpate the bones, they're hard to find. I remember going through it myself. Then we start at the first test of the algorithm and we move through. I'll teach one section of the algorithm, then demonstration and practice, going through testing, treating, and retesting. Once the participants see it working, I explained how it works, the logic of the algorithms, and how to design your own procedures. Then we slowly go through the whole algorithm. I want people to have a strong sense of how to work the process. We go through the whole lumbar-pelvic algorithm in two and a half days. On the last afternoon, we have a back clinic. We bring in people with bad backs.

LAH: Do the participants work on each other?

JdM: They do. But you may have noticed, your colleagues don't have ordinary bodies. We have all had tons of work. I know I have been in session and thought, "This work lots better in class."

LAH: Right, so true.

JdM: So, we bring in people with legitimate bad backs. Everybody gets to do a session on somebody with back pain before they go home. So when somebody hobbles into their office, it's not their first rodeo. I want them to say,

"Okay, I've done this before, I can do this!" The participants work in groups of two with their client, one person is the practitioner. The partner is a faithful servant, working the manual and chart, to get the practitioner the information she needs quickly. The person in the practitioner role will start with step one, the standing flexion test. If they get lost right there, they say to their partner, "I forget." Their partner can easily read the chart to them, show them the picture of the test, and so they work together as a team with one practitioner, one assistant. Then we bring in a second group, the practitioner and assistant change places.

The truth is, it's going to take a session to get you through the algorithm your first few times, but the time it takes becomes less and less with familiarization. If the client has three or four restrictions, it may take the whole session, when it's new. They're going to feel a lot better; they're going to be much happier. When they come back, there may be one restriction left and then you get into your Rolfing series from there.

LAH: That is really cool, you're saying that you bring in the people with random structures that we would normally see.

JdM: More than random, I want people who are hurt! I want models for the class that are hurting because I want participants to leave the class with that direct experience with the hard stuff. I want participants to work in class with somebody that would perhaps scare you if they came to you in your office. It's like, "Let's do it now while I'm here and you can ask me questions. Let's get it done."

LAH: Nice, that is what we have to be able to deal with in our offices, very empowering way to learn.

JdM: What people tell me is that once they have learned this, the word goes out in their community, they are the person to handle a bad back.

LAH: Your class sounds like it streamlines axial interventions that reliably work, are easy to reproduce with each client, and even get to the heart of the matter quicker.

JdM: Hopefully so. I've redesigned the class probably every time I teach it to make it simpler and easier to understand.

LAH: Thank you for your time today and letting our readers know about this valuable perspective.

JdM: You are welcome, and thank you for the work you do on the journal.

John deMahy is a graduate of The Osteopathic College of Ontario, The Dr. Ida Rolf Institute®, and the Louisiana State University School of Nursing. He began his career in orthopedics and emergency nursing. For the last thirty-one years he has had a robust structural integration practice in New Orleans. deMahy taught dance kinesiology at the University of North Carolina-Charlotte. In 2004, he began teaching spinal mobilization using muscle energy technique to structural integrators. Inspired by his emergency department experience, where life often depends on speed and precision, deMahy began developing and teaching Structural Algorithms in 2012.

Lina Amy Hack, BS, BA, SEP, became a Rolfer in 2004 and is now a Certified Advanced Rolfer (2016) practicing in Saskatoon, Saskatchewan, Canada. She has an honors biochemistry degree from Simon Fraser University (2000) and an honors psychology degree from the University of Saskatchewan (2013), as well as a Somatic Experiencing Practitioner (2015) certification. Hack is the Editor-in-Chief of Structure, Function, Integration.

From Skull to Spine, to Sacrum

An Overview of the Axial Complex

By Jan H. Sultan, Advanced Rolfing® Instructor, and Lina Amy Hack, Certified Advanced Rolfer®

ABSTRACT *The axial complex is a specific concept in the Rolfing® Structural Integration paradigm. In this article, Jan H. Sultan presents how Rolfers draw from embryology to conceptualize what anatomy and physiology are represented by the axial complex: the neurocranium, the spine, the sacrum, and their associated soft tissues. Fryette's laws are a useful base when working with axial tissue, as well as Jean-Pierre Barral's, DO, motility concept and John Upledger's, DO, third rhythm. Sultan describes how he synthesizes information to execute the specific technology of Rolfing SI.*

Jan H. Sultan

Lina Amy Hack

Authors' note: This article is written in the voice of Jan H. Sultan. It is a consolidation of many conversations between the two co-authors, putting to the page the Sultan legacy teachings for the Dr. Rolf Institute® (DIRI).

In the context of Rolfing® Structural Integration (SI), the axial complex becomes the place where functional motion restrictions must be integrated. The restoration of blood and lymph flow, and the supporting orientation patterns of better support and gesture also come together here. These elements allow people to be stronger, more stable, less vulnerable, and more adaptable to the demands of life.

Embryological Development of the Axial Complex

The embryological perspective helps us understand the role of the axial complex, whether you have a child or an adult in front of you. When evaluating structure, we need to look to the axial complex and understand the relative order in this vital subsystem.

When the ovum is fertilized, the zygote has the familiar look of an egg. It's got a nucleus at the deepest aspect, it's got the middle cytoplasmic layer, and it's got an outer layer, the cellular membrane. As that embryonic egg divides, mitosis leads to a ball of hundreds of cells. There are the deep

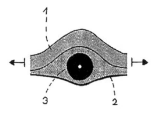

Figure 1: Axial process with notochord in black (transverse view). 1. Ectoderm, 2. Endoderm, 3. Notochord. Illustrations are redrawn from originals, all from different publications by Dr. Erich Blechschmidt, used with permission.

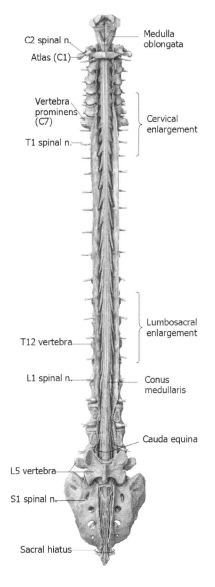

C2 spinal n.
Atlas (C1)
Medulla oblongata

Vertebra prominens (C7)
Cervical enlargement
T1 spinal n.

Lumbosacral enlargement
T12 vertebra

L1 spinal n.
Conus medullaris

Cauda equina
L5 vertebra

S1 spinal n.

Sacral hiatus

Figure 2: Axial complex without the neurocranium. Posterior view, spinous processes and transverse processes cut away, showing the neural tissue within the neural tube. Copyright Thieme Medical Publishers, Inc 2017.

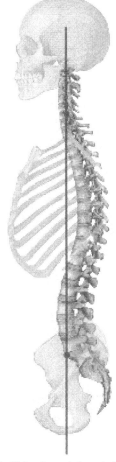

Figure 3: Side view of the skull, spine, and sacrum with right-ribs and right-pelvis showing. Vertical line of gravity also visible. Copyright Thieme Medical Publishers, Inc 2017.

center cells, called the endoderm (inner skin); a community of cells that occupy a loose fluid-filled middle, the mesoderm (middle skin); and the place where we touch, feel, and interface with outside of self, the ectoderm (outer skin). These preliminary three layers form the basis of a whole series of ideas that we want to examine about how structure unfolds.

The embryo reaches a certain point where part of the ectoderm differentiates into neuroectoderm. The ectoderm thickens along a determined line and cavitates inward, the outside moves into the form and becomes the central neural tube. As this happens, the embryo looks like a hot dog instead of a three-layered ball. That hotdog-looking aspect of the central neural tube is destined to become the central nervous system. Ventral to the neural tube, there is a flexible rod of mesodermal cells, these cells collect along the ventral length of the neural tube and are called the primitive notochord

(see Figure 1). The notochord is the central axis of organization where the dorsal aspect will differentiate to become the vertebral bodies and vertebral discs. Note that the spinal cord will eventually arise dorsally to the vertebral bodies, in the spinal nerve canal (see Figure 2). Second note, I often talk about bony landmarks, but I mean for you to include in your mind all the particular bits of softer tissues that are associated with that region as the 'associated soft tissues'. To name a bone is to mark a spot on the map – it's not the territory.

Meanwhile, going ventral to the notochord is a different collection of mesodermal tissue that becomes the visceral space, into which form the organs and investing membranes that hang from the spine. This visceral layer is continuous to the 'tail' of the notochord and has continuity right up to the head and includes the jaw. Oddly enough, the small bones of the ear are part of the vertebral column and also differentiate with the axial complex.

We can think of the axial complex as the skull, the spine, and the sacrum (see Figure 3). Developmentally, the sacrum is part of the axial complex, being made up of five vertebrae that are fused, and the coccyx, which articulates on the sacrum's inferior apex (see Figure 4). One distinct characteristic of mammals is that the tail continues past the anus. What humans are left with is that little tail of a coccyx that we share with other mammals.

Differentiating Core, Sleeve, and Axial

In order to view the axial complex through the Rolfing lens, we've got to place it contextually as part of the primary embryological Five Taxonomies: the shoulder girdle and arms, the pelvic girdle and legs, the visceral spaces containing the organs, the sleeve as immediate structural permitter of the visceral space, and the axial complex (neurocranium, spine, and sacrum). Describing how we assess the axial complex during a body reading means first acknowledging the relationships it has with both girdles and the internal visceral spaces. Finally, it is essential to see that the axial complex functions as sleeve in its role as a boundary structure of the visceral space (core). The axial complex functions as sleeve to the visceral space as well as being the spine proper.

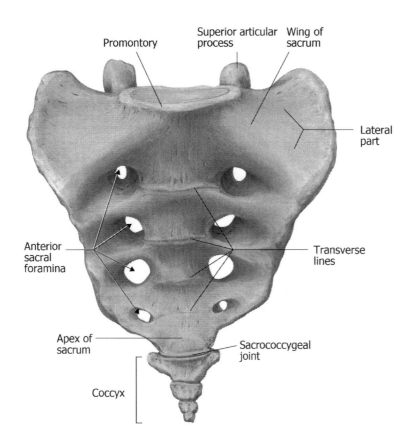

Figure 4: Ventral face of the sacrum. The transverse lines illustrate the five fused vertebral segments that make up the sacrum. Copyright Thieme Medical Publishers, Inc 2017.

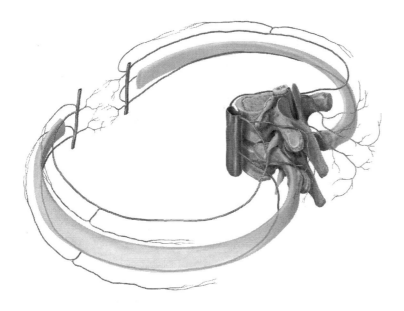

Figure 5: Ribs act like spacers and struts, part of the sleeve aspect of the Five Taxonomies. Copyright Thieme Medical Publishers, Inc 2017.

As a pioneer, Ida P. Rolf (IPR), PhD, struggled to define her work and identify it as a new synthesis. She said something like this, "When I'm working with someone, and the body reaches a certain level of order, its form gains differentiation between its inside and its outside." At one point she described, this inside/outside quality being like an armature in a field inside a generator. To generate electricity, the armature spins inside a stable cylinder. At another time she said, "It is something like a core and a sleeve." There is a problem with the word *core* because the word is quite abstract. When listeners hear the word, they will go to widely diverse definitions in their minds. Some people will think core function, others core values, and so on.

One of Rolf's mandates was that if you are going to use an abstraction you have to ground it. In this light, it was clear to me that the word *core* is a very ungrounded abstraction. After several years I changed this definition of the internal spaces to 'visceral space'. I abandoned 'core' as a descriptor of the organized body. It turns out being able to identify and quantify the visceral space is a useful way to analyze people's structure. If I'm compressed in my thoracic visceral space, the space becomes diminished, and my abdominal viscera is pressurized downward. Or if I suck my gut in and I lift my sternum, I've shifted the volume of my viscera upward. One of the emergent qualities of a balanced body is an even distribution of the visceral space volume, contained by sleeve structures and the axial complex. The darling 'core' is now in its place as a functional metaphor and not a literal anatomic unit.

A similar semantic problem exists with the concept of 'sleeve'. There is no sleeve per se, except as the visceral space has boundary structures throughout the body that defines that space. This is how the concept is used, as a part of the perception of the visceral space, like a jar contains and defines the space inside it. The ventral surface of the ribs then are sleeve because they participate in defining the shape of the abdomen and thorax. The ilia have a function as sleeve in that they define the inside shape of the pelvis. Consider an ilium; in one way the ilium is part of the leg, another way to see it is part of the pelvic ring, and a third way is as sleeve, as a boundary structure of the visceral space of the pelvis.

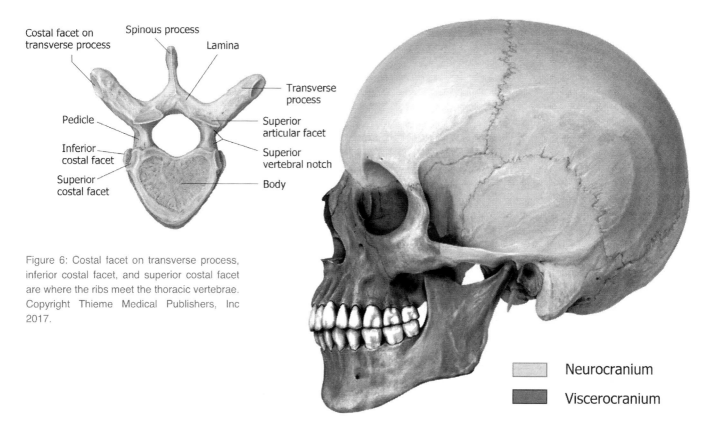

Figure 6: Costal facet on transverse process, inferior costal facet, and superior costal facet are where the ribs meet the thoracic vertebrae. Copyright Thieme Medical Publishers, Inc 2017.

Neurocranium

Viscerocranium

Figure 7: Axial complex includes the neurocranium, not the viscerocranium. Copyright Thieme Medical Publishers, Inc 2017.

And what about ribs? When I look in medical orthopedic books, the rib cage is classified with the spine as axial. Embryologically, the ribs are not from the same layers of tissue. From this view, ribs are sleeve structures. The ribs form from ossification centers within the mesoderm. As this tissue organizes, the ribs show up as struts and spacers (see Figure 5). Dorsally, as the ribs come around the back, they articulate on the inner aspect of the transverse processes. This makes a sleeve/axial junction at the costotransverse meeting points. Finally, the rib heads butt up against two vertebrae with a hemi-facet on each corresponding vertebra (see Figure 6). The deep surface of the rib head has continuity with the lateral aspect of the fibers of the intervertebral disc.

The Axial Complex is the Neurocranium, Spine, and Sacrum

To restate the premise and keep the visceral space/sleeve structures in mind, what is the axial complex? Let's consider

Rolf's 'upper pole' of the human form, you're really looking at the intersection of the visceral tube and the neurocranium (Hack and Sultan 2021). The visceral layers of the cranium, the face, belong with the gut. The bones of the vault, the neural tissue of the brain, and the spinal cord go with the spine (see Figure 7). The viscerocranium is the jaw, the palate, and as I like to say, the associated soft tissues. They are a different layer than the axial complex.

Next consider the spine, with the associated soft tissues that draw the attention of Rolfers, this includes the intervertebral and paraspinal ligament beds. Of interest is the cluster of soft tissues that are immediately adjacent to either side of the laminar groove, the costal connections, and costotransverse junctions. These should always be considered as part of the axial complex. Deep to the erectors, these tiny ligamentous muscles organize the interaction of the vertebrae and ribs. If you dissected a dozen people, you'd find some people's intertransversarii and costotransverse are ligaments, while they are more like tiny muscles in other people

(see Figure 8). Add the intervertebral fasciae as well, which is vertebra to vertebra. There is probably a lot of variation between people in the amount of red meat they may have within these deep fascial layers. The anatomy books are general maps, and the individuals have variations in morphology. Anything we do with the spine immediately goes to the ribs by virtue of this layering.

At the upper pole, as previously mentioned, the visceral space and the axial complex converge. This happens as well at the lower pole, the pelvis. There is no pelvis when we really consider this perspective, as in the head, the pelvis is a meeting place of systems. We already talked about how the sacrum and spine develop from the notochord. The ilia in turn develop with the legs, and they are leg structures that articulate on the sacrum. If you look at the sacroiliac joints, they are a bridge between the axial and the appendicular, the sacrum can articulate on the ilia as an aspect of leg function, and the ilia can articulate on the sacrum as an aspect of spinal function. (see Figure 9). The pelvic visceral space

Ultimately, there is no axial complex distinct from the whole body, but there are rules about the axial complex and its relationship to the sleeve.

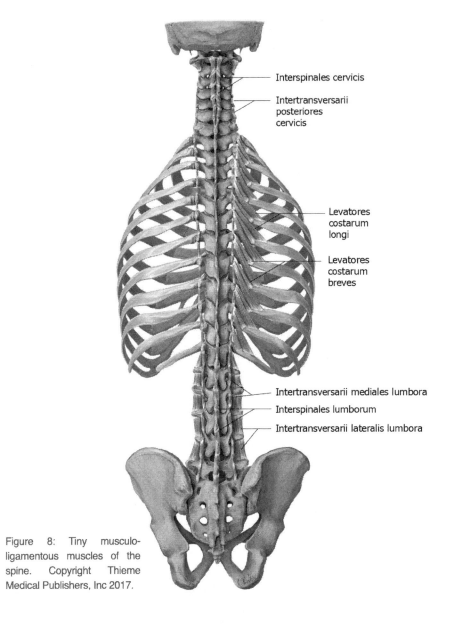

Figure 8: Tiny musculo-ligamentous muscles of the spine. Copyright Thieme Medical Publishers, Inc 2017.

Interspinales cervicis

Intertransversarii posteriores cervicis

Levatores costarum longi

Levatores costarum breves

Intertransversarii mediales lumbora

Interspinales lumborum

Intertransversarii lateralis lumbora

contains the organs of reproduction and elimination. The sleeve structures of the pelvis are the ilia, abdominal wall, and pelvic floor; while the axial complex at the level of the pelvis is the terminus of the spine and sacrum (with all its neural outflows). Coherent organization of this region has to include all of these systems, all while holding the idea that the ilia are legs, the sacrum is axial, and they interact functionally as a pelvis.

Ultimately, there is no axial complex distinct from the whole body, but there are rules about the axial complex and its relationship to the sleeve. The critical bit is where the spine meets the sleeve (the costovertebral and costotransverse junctions), where the sacrum meets the ilia. When you can see the spine in relation to its immediate components, then your ability to work with the spine will improve enormously.

Fryette's Laws of Spinal Mechanics

Rolfing SI has adopted the standardized nomenclature for spinal mechanics from the osteopathic profession. These rules are called Fryette's laws (Fryette 1980). The foundation is that all spinal motion is coupled with both sidebending and rotation. These two movements co-occur in all the spinal movements we do. Type I spinal movement is when the spine sidebends in one direction, there is a simultaneous rotation of the vertebral bodies in the opposite direction. As the spine is sidebent to the right, the vertebral bodies will rotate left, away from that compression. Type II movement in Fryette's laws happens when the spine is sidebent to the same side as the vertebral rotation. Fryette's laws describe cervical vertebrae functioning as Type II in their normal function. As the neck sidebends left, the vertebral bodies will also rotate to the left.

If you sidebend the sacrum to the right, the sacrum can't rotate around a vertical axis because of the shape of the two sacroiliac joints being crescents facing dorsally. But the sacrum will sidebend and then it'll rotate on a diagonal axis away from the compression side. So, the sacrum is Type I, with a variant that it has a diagonal axis rather than a horizontal axis (see Figure 10).

Fryette's laws are a good, rough guide to understanding the spine, and form the basis for evaluating both single vertebra positions, and group patterns of vertebrae as well. For example, imagine a person has two vertebrae that are left rotated and right sidebent in the middle of their neutral spine. The person reports that the area is uncomfortable. If it happens in the thorax, this pattern can also take the ribs with it. As the vertebra rotates from neutral to left rotated, the ribs on the right are going to move deeper and the ribs on the left are going to be more posterior. Right away, in this case, there is a complex of strain. Fryette's laws give us a foundation for a whole body of techniques that are called positional release.

Let's consider that example further, my client having two vertebrae rotated left in the middle of the rib cage might be in pain as well. This pattern happened when they fell off their bicycle. This spine couldn't get back to neutral. If I put this person face down on the table and I put them into a left sidebend, it puts pressure

Figure 9: Lateral view of the sacrum. Copyright Thieme Medical Publishers, Inc 2017.

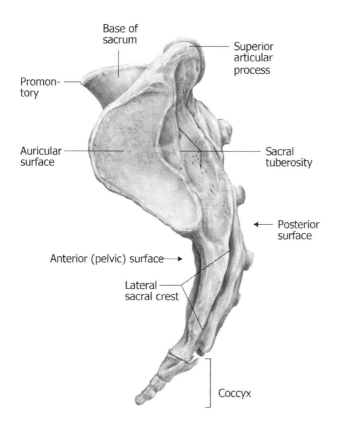

Base of
sacrum

Promon-
tory

Superior
articular
process

Auricular
surface

Sacral
tuberosity

Posterior
surface

Anterior (pelvic) surface

Lateral
sacral crest

Coccyx

and ask for movement." The idea was that the voluntary movement, guided by the practitioner's hands, would anchor the change into the nervous system and proprioception. Having said that, the more I think about this work, the more firmly I think that mobility is a biological priority over position. As a student of Rolf, then I started thinking as if position was the law, and I much later came to understand that a prerequisite of position was the inherent mobility of the tissues. The basic idea is that if the structure moves appropriately, then the body will function relatively pain-free. Bringing the parts to have better relationships will enhance function. Structural integration then is a hierarchical two-step process, first establish mobility and then encourage position.

This seemingly small change of perception shifted my technique to the extent that I'm not a straight IPR Rolfer. To explain the Ten Series, in order to respect the variables involved in transforming tissue manually, the Dr. Ida Rolf Institute® (DIRI) faculty had to advance the work. The idea we got from Rolf was that the body was like a homogeneous clay that you could mold. Yet modern Rolfing SI owes its substance and potency to the pioneering work that was done in the osteopathic profession. Specifically with our exposure to Jean-Pierre Barral, DO, and John Upledger, DO. In our interactions with them, we came to understand that the body is pulsing, rhythmically expanding and retracting, in a symphony of waveforms. You're jumping into a moving river when you do manual interventions. The body is not a bed of clay that you're mucking about in. In this way, Rolfing SI is syncretic; it has absorbed elements that describe the true nature of human bodily being in more specific and accurate terms than Rolf was able to. My understanding of structure changed post-Rolf to the extent that it's clear that motility gives rise to mobility, and that a better position can and will emerge at higher levels of balance as the underlying tissues become healthy.

It was 1985 when I first had the information about the cranial concept from Upledger and it was probably ten years before it sank all the way into my hands, and I

on the target vertebrae to rotate away from the sidebend. This positioning sets it up so that when I put direct vectored pressure in there and begin to open up the costotransverse joints, that pressure on the vertebrae, preloaded by their position, facilitates the vertebrae to return to neutral.

After you understand the principle of positional release technique, the variants of this technique can look a lot of ways. You could have the client seated on the bench, give them a strategic hug, and you sidebend them. Put the heel of your hand or your thumb on the posterior transverse process and then have the person sidebend, to that side. This is done slowly to functionally rock the restricted unit into motion. Conceptually you're working from the basis of Fryette's laws when coupling rotation and sidebend from the neutral spine position to solve motion restriction and restore easy neutral.

There's a subtext in Fryette's laws that says, if you are in extreme backbending or extreme forward-bending, then your Type Is behave more like Type IIs. This is the blurred edge on Fryette's laws and in part why there's an argument about it. If the client presents with a kyphotic spine, then they are already bent forward. This may bias the predictability of positional release technique. In cases where the structural bias is not from neural, then the motion patterns must be tested and identified before the application of technique to 'normalize' mobility.

Motility Precedes Mobility

When it comes to executing manual interventions with the axial complex, the position of the vertebrae is not the whole story. Rolf had a set of axioms that guided her early practitioners. Paramount among them was the, "Put it where it belongs

You're jumping into a moving river when you do manual interventions. The body is not a bed of clay that you're mucking about in.

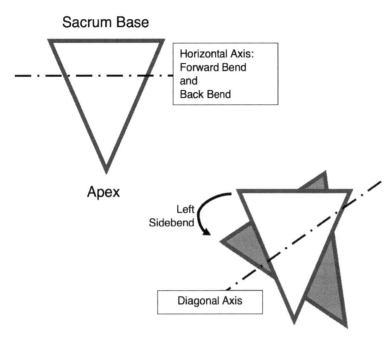

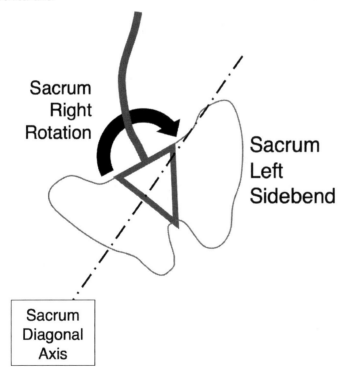

Figure 10: Triangle represents the posterior view of the sacrum. While sacrum forward bends and back bends along a horizontal axis, the sacrum sidebends along a diagonal axis, not a vertical axis.

could feel it. Later in my journey, Barral laid this out beautifully in his first book on visceral manipulation, when he articulated the hierarchy of motility, mobility, and position (2005). Rolf didn't specifically name motility. I've gone back through my notes, it's not there. One of her first laws was, "Put it where it belongs and ask for movement." She drilled us on this. Even her early movement exercises were about the combination of position and movement designed to re-educate neural pathways and proprioceptive feedback loops. It was about asking the question, "How do you organize the connections between the elements of the body?"

Compare that with Barral, he says hierarchically, you need motility first, that it is an inherent pulsatory activity of metabolism. If you have good motility, the next priority is to have competent mobility, and then finally, if things move to their ideal position, then you've got another layer of potential better function. The concept of motility utterly rearranged how I think about Rolfing SI. As soon as I went to motility as the highest order of biological need and began to understand how mobility arises from motility, my manual technique also changed accordingly. The functionality of the human body must include motility to work.

I credit Upledger for breaking me loose from Rolf's clay concept. The thing that Upledger brought to us in the 1980s, from the osteopathic perspective, is that the body is pulsating (Upledger and Vredevoogd 1983). The body has waveforms that are part of its being. Upledger described a new-to-me innate movement that was clearly palpable as separate from the cardiac pulse, respiratory pulse, and peristalsis. This waveform is yet something else. One of its indicators was the pulsation of the circulation of the cerebrospinal fluid. That was just a palpable part of it. There was another part that had to be bioenergetic, that there were fluctuations in the field of the organism's existence.

Between Upledger's cranial rhythm and Barral's motility, mobility, position hierarchy, it was never the same to touch a person. I had more information in my hands, both about the whole structure, as well as the axial complex specifically. This mastery wasn't in how Rolf trained me. With this knowledge I had an enhanced spectrum of manual therapy technology that emerged out of this intersection

Disorganized or motion-restricted spines can appear dense, immobile, asymmetrical, or compressed. We love to talk about the lumbodorsal hinge, the mid-thoracic hinge, but what does this mean? A hinge is a functional concept, a high-level abstraction, and it follows perpendicular to 'the Line' as the organization of horizontal planes.

between osteopathy and Rolfing SI. For me, it was like coming home.

Body Reading the Axial Complex

When doing a body reading, there is a point where I isolate the organization of the axial complex. But I start with putting somebody on a 'lazy Susan' turntable in my mind, and I turn them to get a sense of the whole body. I'm not just looking at the front, back, left side, and right side, but I'm rotating them. I'm asking the Five Taxonomies question: What is happening with the shoulder girdle, the pelvic girdle, visceral space, sleeve, and axial relationships in gravity? I also watch the person's normal walking gait to gather information about how they go through space. When I get to the axial component, it's not just looking at the spine, but it's looking at the relationship of the spine to the other components. It all starts with our first Principle of Intervention, wholism (Sultan and Hack 2021). Ultimately, there is no axial complex distinct from the whole body, but there are rules about the axial complex and its relationship to the sleeve, especially the sacroiliac joints, costovertebral and costotransverse junctions.

Disorganized or motion-restricted spines can appear dense, immobile, asymmetrical, or compressed. We love to talk about the lumbodorsal hinge, the mid-thoracic hinge, but what does this mean? A hinge is a functional concept, a high-level abstraction, and it follows perpendicular to 'the Line' as the organization of horizontal planes. If you see a person whose mid-thoracic hinge is working, you will also see better head carriage. You would see more flow through the thoracic spine when the heels strike the ground. You'd see the

movement carry through the spine. But if you ask anatomically what's a hinge, you're stuck. Hinge was a concept as a functional domain of inquiry. Out of the Line came the hinges and the horizontals.

What does a well-adapted axial complex look like? What we can observe here is this delicate intersection of the physiology of the spine, the neural outflows, and the kinesiology of locomotion interacting to create a pelvis and its associated soft tissues that move consistently with its genotypical limits. When a Rolfer sees a pelvis that has an anterior tilt, on deeper reflection, they may find that one ilium has an anterior torsion on the sacrum and the other one is in a relative posterior torsion. This would create a twist that runs through the unit on a horizontal axis. Add that to the anterior tilt of the postural context of the whole unit and a more comprehensive clinical pattern emerges.

Keep in mind that we're made to absorb a certain amount of asymmetry and to remain quite functional. It has to be that way because living tissue has to have a little free play. It doesn't have to be perfect; it has to be able to move through. We must be able to make a distinction between asymmetry and dysfunction. If the component of interest continues to be able to move, it will work well. The organism will be supported and able to do survival behaviors.

When somebody was better organized in Rolf's terms, what we were observing was the mobility of the whole body. That there was a certain quality of radiance and a continuity would emerge, there was an evenness to the form of the body. Looking at the shape of the person, nothing stuck out, and everything was present. Discontinuity shows up because our primitive eye is always looking for something out of place. I now think that the increased radiance is a function of underlying motility that has emerged.

A fundamental part of training a Rolfer is to teach 'seeing', the Rolfer's gaze is to do a visual analysis that looks for discontinuity or lack of symmetry in the client's body. This stands out once you are tuned to see it as an indicator of underlying structural strain. When someone's body has natural continuity, they also have radiating mobility. This shows up in the natural athletes, in the person who can move gracefully without thinking about it. Some people have been born with the trait of continuity and then work tirelessly to express it.

Once you see how a client's axial complex is arranged and you want to bring each data point collected from your body reading to bear on your manual interventions, the goal is a more neutral expression with overall better congruence. This point of view changes your tactics on how you go about working with the spine. The spine is not a stuck vertebra. The spine is not a curvature. The axial complex is this embedded system involved in the expression of this whole individual's contour. Even the extremities will express curvature patterns before you ever look at the spine. By virtue of how the arms and the legs are working, you can see the pattern of the individual across the room. Because all spinal patterns are also expressed in the extremities. So as a rule, if you're going to work on the axial complex, you must decompensate the extremities, or they will keep pushing the original information back towards the spine. You can try and 'fix the spine' or 'mobilize the spine', but if you don't get the extremities to take the step of being able to integrate and support what you're doing in the spine, the extremities are going to drive the pattern right back otherwise. This is pure Rolf.

Conclusion

When it comes to the axial complex, we always come back to that ligament bed thinking, of all those tiny ligament bed muscles, contacting in between transitional structures. They have got to be hydrated – motility. I put people sidelying on a pillow and I put my elbow in that spinal groove, I chisel and I have them lift up and forward, lift up and go back. Eventually, it's about restoring this mobility. Ultimately, with our Rolfing work, we are focused on the restoration of function like our peers the osteopaths. But what makes Rolfing SI distinct is that we also work to get people in a better place structurally, so that they are more stable, more supported from below, more adaptable. It isn't restoration alone; it is real enhancement.

Jan H. Sultan's initial encounter with Dr. Rolf was in 1967 as her client. In 1969 he trained under her. In 1975, after assisting several classes, Rolf invited him to become an instructor. After further apprenticeship, she invited him to take on the Advanced Training. Over the next ten years, Sultan taught several Advanced Trainings with Peter Melchior, Emmett Hutchins, Michael Salveson, and other faculty members, collaborating on refinements to the Advanced Training. Sultan currently teaches Basic Trainings, continuing education, and Advanced Trainings for the Dr. Ida Rolf Institute and continuing education to the extended SI community. He feels strongly that his responsibility as an instructor goes beyond simply passing on what he was taught, but also includes the development of the ideas and methodology taught by Rolf.

Lina Amy Hack, BS, BA, SEP, became a Rolfer in 2004 and is now a Certified Advanced Rolfer (2016) practicing in Saskatoon, Saskatchewan, Canada. She has an honors biochemistry degree from Simon Fraser University (2000) and an honors psychology degree from the University of Saskatchewan (2013), as well as a Somatic Experiencing® Practitioner (2015) certification. Hack is the Editor-in-Chief of Structure, Function, Integration.

References

Barral, Jean-Pierre, and Pierre Mercier. 2005. *Visceral Manipulation.* Seattle, WA: Eastland Press.

Fryette, Harrison H. 1980. *Principles of Osteopathic Technic.* Indianapolis, IN: American Academy of Osteopathy.

Hack, L. A. and J. H. Sultan. 2021. At the head of the table: An interview with Jan Sultan. *Structure, Function, Integration* 49(1):14-20.

Sultan, J. H. and L. A. Hack. 2021. The Rolfing SI principles of intervention: An integrated concept. *Structure, Function, Integration* 49(3):16-24.

Upledger, John E. and Jon D. Vredevoogd.1983. *Craniosacral Therapy.* Seattle, WA: Eastland Press.

Dr.Ida Rolf Institute®
Journal Ad Layout Card

AD SPECS

Full page
Trim: 8.5 x 11"
Bleed: 9 x 11.5"
Safe area:

Double page spread (DPS)
Trim: 17 x 11"
Bleed: 17.5 x 11.5"
Safe area:

Third page
3 x 11"

Half page verticle
4.25 x 11"

Half page horizontal
8.5 x 5.5"

Quarter page
4.25 x 5.5"

Please supply files as a high-resolution PDF required. Photos at 300dpi, greyscale only are accepted.
Please contact Lina Amy Hack at linabehie@hotmail.com for pricing and submissions.

Interpreting Anatomy Illustrations

2016 Fascia Research Summer School Report and Insights

By Luiz Fernando Bertolucci, MD, Basic Rolfing® Instructor

Luiz Fernando Bertolucci

ABSTRACT *Rolfing® faculty member Fernando Bertolucci reflects on his experience at the Fascia Research Summer School (FRSS) held in Leipzig, Germany. Bertolucci specifically focuses on the construction of anatomy images and the difference between fascia-oriented dissection images and organ-oriented dissection images.*

This article is based on my experience at the Fascia Research Summer School (FRSS) held in Leipzig, Germany, in September 2016, where I had the honor to participate as a grant recipient. I thank the Dr. Ida Rolf Institute® (DIRI) and the University of Leipzig for making such an opportunity available. Below are some pieces of information I found interesting and useful to the Rolfing Structural Integration (SI) context, along with some insights I had.

Jaap van der Wal, MD, PhD, is a medical doctor, and before his retirement in 2012, he was an associate professor in anatomy and embryology at the University of Maastricht, Holland. I want to highlight van der Wal's point of view that he presented for his FRSS presentation of

fascial anatomy, very much in line with the Rolfing perspective of wholism. He has a helpful understanding of the role of fascia in motion, and his insights can inform us about our practice as Rolfers®. The human starting point is embryological development where our bodies have no *'parts'* and anatomy (meaning literally to 'cut up') is about cutting, separating, locating, and naming *parts*. This anatomical point of view may be helpful to show more or less identifiable *parts* during dissection, as is the case of an organ such as the liver, for instance. But when one aims their attention to the tissues *in between* those parts (fascia), such a method becomes inappropriate.

Fascia is continuous throughout the body and one of its main features is putting

The scalpel could work as a pencil to draw the frame of mind of the anatomist. Considering the omnipresence of the connective tissue, each and every separation by an anatomist will be artificial and already disruptive to the original continuity.

parts *in relation* to one another and, in so being, having no clear boundaries. In this article I will present van der Wal's 'dynament' concept (van der Wal 2009). In short, this has to do with the relationship between musculoskeletal motor function and fascia, that integrated function of the body's movable units, and how these relationships allow forces to travel among body parts. Separating parts, as is done to produce anatomy images for study, distorts the behavior of the system and hampers the understanding of its function. The scientific method usually separates parts to study them, but how can one learn a system whose functions depend on its *continuity*?

Anatomical View

Let us start with the unfoldings of the 'anatomical' view present in anatomy illustrations. Van der Wal shows that many anatomy illustrations in commonly used books are faulty representations of the fascial anatomy and its organization (or *architecture*, as discussed below). This may occur because, when dissecting, the anatomist already has an idea of what is supposed to be found and can often 'make up' anatomical structures with the scalpel (sharp dissection) based on such expectations. The scalpel could work as a pencil to draw the frame of mind of the anatomist. Considering the omnipresence of the connective tissue, each and every separation by an anatomist will be artificial and already disruptive to the original continuity. To study what is 'in there', commonly the anatomist disregards fascia, as it may be in their way to study a specific *part*. An anatomist may disregard the wrappings of structures, like one that throws away the wrapping of a present, eager only to know the contents. But the container, as Rolfers knew from long ago, is as essential as the contents and constitutes the environment that such contents inhabit.

Nonetheless, one can perform a *fascia-oriented* dissection to study connective-tissue organization, as opposed to *organ-oriented* dissection. In the 1980s, van der Wal (2020) made fascia-oriented dissections of the forearm and, based on his findings, developed a phenomenological and philosophical view of fascia. This view of fascia integrates and resonates with the Rolfing SI point of view. Below are some examples and reflections about such a view.

1. Ligaments and Tendons: One Continuous System

One example of anatomical 'interpretations' deals with the structures that are responsible for joint stability. The classic concept describes: (a) a *passive* system of ligaments and (b) an *active* system of tendinous structures linked to muscles. With this frame of mind, it is possible that the anatomist 'foresees' such structures and separates them with his scalpel accordingly. Such separation may have artificially 'created' structures that were originally part of a continuous system.

In his fascia-sparing studies of the forearm, van der Wal did not find any *separation*, proximally, between the tendinous and ligamentous structures. They seemed to be all part of the same connective-tissue complex to which the muscles converge, in a complex but continuous system. Just like the rotator cuffs described in the shoulder, he describes this same type of structure embracing the epicondyles and inserting into the bone, including, in an uninterrupted way, structures formerly described as joint capsule, ligaments, and tendons. In other words, what is described in the anatomy books as collateral elbow ligaments may be all part of the dense connective tissues that connect the muscle fibers to the bones.

Likewise, the same could be true for the annular ligament that is part of the supinator muscle. Sharp dissection can 'make' an annular ligament. Previous anatomists' knowledge may steer their mind to use the scalpel to 'find' the so-called annular ligament. Van der Wal's *fascia sparing dissections* showed no boundaries between such structures.

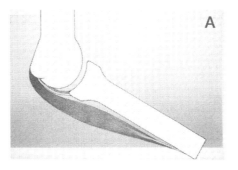
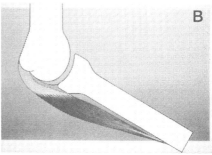

Figure 1: Many anatomy book illustrations depict muscle (darker grey) and capsular ligaments (lighter grey) as being discrete structures that lie in parallel with one another (A). Van der Wal and other anatomists have shown that muscle (dark grey), tendon, and capsular ligaments (lighter grey) all make part of the same system and lie in series with one another. This would allow tension to be present all along the range of motion of a joint, and hence continuously feeding the central nervous system with proprioceptive information (B).

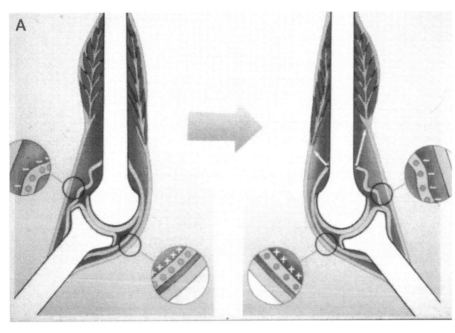

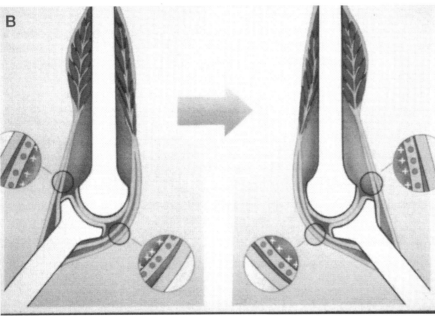

Figure 2: The traditional the concept of ligaments is that they are passive structures lying in parallel with tendons. They would be slack (---) and tense (+++) depending on the position of a joint, i.e., the system would turn on and off (A). If ligaments and tendons are part of the same system, there will be a certain degree of tension throughout the range of movement of a joint. The mechanoreceptors would then be able to convey proprioceptive information continuously (+++) (B).

2. Ligaments and Tendons: In-Parallel or In-Series Structures?

The classic anatomical separation between ligaments and tendons also considers these structures as functionally distinct: to achieve joint stability, 'passive' ligaments lay *in parallel* with 'active' tendons (see Figure 1). Van der Wal showed that in this continuous system of connective tissue linking the muscles to the bones, what has been described as 'ligaments', is laid down in fact, *in series* with the 'tendons' in one single, continuous structure.

The biomechanical view to describe ligaments in parallel is that they are slack when their bones are brought together and then become taut when their associated bones move apart from each other. For example, ligaments undergo tensile stresses [and hence become able to convey proprioceptive afferents to the central nervous system (CNS)] only in certain joint positions (see Figure 2). It follows from this logic that the proprioceptive source would be turned on and off depending on joint position, which would not seem to be an ingenious choice by nature. But, if ligaments and tendons were all part of the same continuous structure, there would also be a *continuous* tension in the system, signaling proprioceptive afferents to the CNS along the whole range of motion (ROM). The latter would possibly be associated with a richer dynamic control of joint stability, as opposed to a system that turns on and off.

This concept is useful for us Rolfing SI practitioners, to imagine *continuous* tension within the whole connective-tissue structure along the ROM of a joint. Then we can include this as a possible element for working with appropriate proprioceptive afferents and hence contributing to good movement quality. Our intervention would help ameliorate the *distribution* of such tension, which may work in two cooperative ways: first with better proprioceptive information and better effectors (joints, muscles etc.) and second, refined performance (i.e., when the structure is moving in a higher degree of tensile integration, as discussed below).

3. Pennate Muscle Architecture: Intramuscular Tendons and Intermuscular Septa

An aspect often neglected in anatomy book illustrations is the *type of muscle-fiber arrangement*. In many current anatomy books, the drawings of the

Figure 3: Oblique vanes of a feather. Photo by Jasmin Sessler on Unsplash.

forearm muscles show muscle fibers oriented longitudinally to the muscle belly and also continuing longitudinally to the tendon and then to the bone. A closer look will show that the muscle fibers of these muscles have an *oblique* arrangement respective to the tendinous structures, which proximally is the antebrachial fascia itself. Van der Wal's studies showed that in the proximal third of the forearm, the muscle fibers are inserted in the *inner* surface of the antebrachial fascia, which is considered an *aponeurotic* fascia for this reason. (Aponeurosis is a flat tendon.) Such aponeurotic fascia wraps the condyles and inserts into the epicondyle of the humerus. On the other end, distally, the muscle fibers of the forearm insert into dense tendons that are present within the muscle bellies (the so-called intramuscular tendons and/or intermuscular septa). The organization of muscle fibers, inserting obliquely in their tendons, resembles a feather (see Figure 3), and so they are described as *pennate* muscles (*pena* Latin for feather).

The intramuscular tendons converge as they run distally, giving rise to the tendons in the proximal third of the forearm. Such oblique pennate arrangements of muscle fibers are often not represented in anatomy illustrations, giving the false impression of many tendons attach to

the – small – epicondyle area. Rather, the deep antebrachial fascia receives the insertions from the various muscles, just like a rotator cuff. Van der Wal coined these structures lateral and medial force transmission systems, and they stabilize the elbow in a similar way that the rotator cuff does in the shoulder.

In fact, such continuity between tendinous and ligamentous structures has been described for the shoulder's rotator cuff by Jobe and Coen (2004). One can say, then, that the antebrachial fascia has muscle attachments in its proximal third, i.e., it *links or connects* structures in this region. Palpation of this area has a fleshy feeling of the muscles, and if one strums transversally, it is possible to notice the myofascial compartments moving in relation to one another.

4. Same Name and Diverse Functions: Antebrachial Fascia

In contrast with the proximal third, in the distal third of the forearm, dense antebrachial fascia *encases* the tendons (of the same muscles it proximally gave rise to) and permits their gliding underneath. Note that here the antebrachial fascia has a different role than the proximal third. It creates room or *disconnects* structures instead of having the connecting role just described in its proximal third. Palpating this area, one can notice the rope-like tendons moving in relation to each other in the areolar planes of connective tissue contiguous with the dense plane of the antebrachial fascia. So, the same structure, the antebrachial fascia, has different functions depending on the region concerned: proximally, it serves as an attachment site for muscle fibers on its inner surface and *connects* structures, and distally, it creates room (or acts to *disconnect* structures) for the tendons to glide freely.

This observation of the antebrachial fascia relationships is interesting to people doing Rolfing SI and related manual approaches. Suppose we consider manual fascia-oriented manipulation affecting areolar tissue and encouraging gliding of neighboring structures. In that case, we can deduce one key area that should be worked is the middle third of the forearm. In other words, Rolfers' fascial interventions can affect the connection/disconnection qualities of the relationships with neighboring structures, and the middle third of the forearm is

the area where the transition occurs between these two opposite functions. Dense tissue and adhesions would be more likely to happen where the two polar fascia roles of connection/disconnection interchange.

It is noteworthy to mention that the distal third of the antebrachial fascia, besides disconnecting structures to allow tendons to glide, also works connecting structures in another fashion. Near the wrist, this fascial structure is reinforced and constitutes the so-called retinacula. Such structures have, in this sense, a linking role, as they maintain the tendons near the bone during wrist movements. This is another example of how anatomists can 'make structures' with their scalpels as the retinacula are often depicted as discrete structures in anatomy books, and yet, they are reinforcements of the antebrachial fascia and continuous with it. Considering the above features together, one can imagine how the study of fascia is a challenge, and the classic *cutting* anatomical methods have limitations.

5. Integrating Fascia Anatomy and Fascia Architecture

As we've covered, anatomists dissect and separate structures, they locate structures and give them names. But the connective tissue is continuous all over the organism, lying within and in between structures, and this is what makes anatomy study particularly difficult. Each and every anatomist's 'cut' is artificial and may 'create' a structure that *in vivo* is not separate from the rest, a fact that may hamper the understanding of the body structures' real relationships and functions. To address this issue, van der Wal talks about the notion of *fascia architecture*, instead of fascia anatomy (2009). The latter would describe *where* structures are while the former describes *how* the structures are functionally related.

In the anatomy lab it is common to hear things such as "I will 'clean' this area up, so we can better see what is within." But *cleaning up* means taking off the fascia, especially the areolar tissue, and the original structural relationships that existed among neighbor structures are now severed and cannot be appreciated anymore. This has been happening more and more in the recent years, authors and illustrators want to give as 'clear' an idea as possible to the readers of the anatomy structures. In doing so, many such

Nice and 'clean' illustrations may be useful to show some aspects of anatomy, but they are biased by our previous knowledge and expectations, they should be seen as so.

illustrations carry their *interpretations* of what supposedly is to be seen. Nice and 'clean' illustrations may be useful to show some aspects of anatomy, but they are biased by our previous knowledge and expectations, and that should be noted. As the importance of the connecting/ disconnecting role of the connective tissue has been valued only recently, the anatomy books that show such features are recent or yet to be published.

It is worth mentioning that being at the FRSS exposed the participants to the work developed by the anatomy team at Leipzig University, where they had specially prepared cadavers that were pliable and the tissue looked fresh. These were a great resource in studying the relationships among parts established by the connective tissue. By the end of the FRSS week, we were also presented with an exhibition of wonderful photos to be part of a published fascia atlas. Such endeavors will give us a progressively better understanding of the role of fascia in integrating body parts.

One can have an idea of how cutting-anatomy procedures interfere with the integrative role of fascia. In one paper, the group around Peter A. Huijing, PhD, performed a 'progressive dissection' from the skin to the deeper tissues while monitoring the forces acting in the muscles underneath (Huijing, Maas, and Baan 2003). Interestingly, just cutting the skin already changes the forces in the tendons lying deep in the rat paw!

6. Endo and Exoskeletons: Means to Distribute Forces?

Mammals have bony endoskeletons, which are moved by the muscles that lie outside them. The classic biomechanical view is that we move segments through moving their bones, which are pulled by the tendons attached to them (muscle-tendon-bone path of force transmission). But we know now that the fascia system is also linked to the muscles and integrates their function through the *myofascial force transmission* path. Dense aponeurotic fascia constitutes a whole system where the muscles are also connected, then in turn, to the osseous skeleton through the intermuscular septa. We can then envision a whole 'fibrous skeleton' with spaces occupied by muscles (and organs). Van der Wal suggested the idea of a 'connective-tissue skeleton', a concept also described by Bienfait as a 'fibrous skeleton' (Bienfait 1987). In this view, our bodies could be considered a structure composed of a softer fibrous skeleton and a more rigid osseous skeleton.

Such a 'fibrous or connective-tissue skeleton' encompasses structures in various depths: more superficial (near the skin) structures, such as the antebrachial fascia or the thoracolumbar fascia, as well as deeper ones (such as intermuscular septa). Consider the existence of muscle attachments in the *inner* surface of aponeurotic dense fascia, as described above in the forearm, as well as myofascial expansions (such as the lacertus fibrosus), richly described by Stecco (2015). One may conceive that the aponeurotic dense fascia can somehow also have an *exoskeleton* capacity, as it also encompasses more superficial dense fascial structures (although such structures are considered deep fascia, as opposed to superficial fascia). One such example would be the gluteus maximus, which has two portions, a deeper one that inserts to the great trochanter (muscle-bone path) and a more superficial one, attaching to the posterior portion of the iliotibial

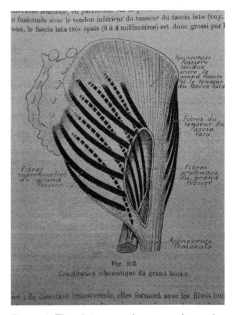

Figure 4: The gluteus maximus muscle can be subdivided into two layers: a deep one, inserting to the greater trochanter and a superficial one, inserting to the iliotibial tract; both move the hip, the former via the osseous skeleton and the latter via the deep fascia, which could be considered a kind of 'exoskeleton'. The distribution of forces within the system would make it more resistant to possible mechanical overload, the main cause of musculoskeletal disorders (Testut 1909).

Van der Wal suggested the idea of a 'connective-tissue skeleton', a concept also described by Bienfait as a 'fibrous skeleton'. In this view, our bodies could be considered a structure composed of a softer fibrous skeleton and a more rigid osseous skeleton.

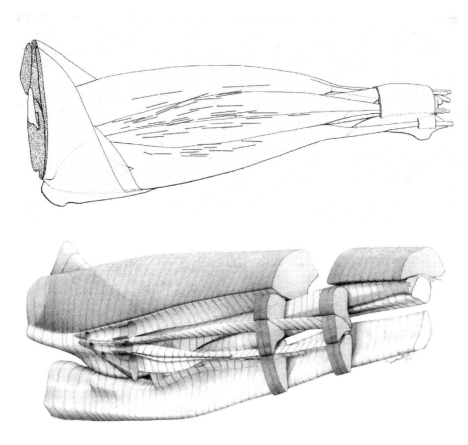

Figure 5: The muscular zones dense in muscle spindles (short grey lines in the upper image) are the stress- and force-conveying zones of the myofascial structures. They concentrate mainly in the interfaces between tissues with various mechanical properties (e.g., muscle and dense connective tissue structures) where tissue deformation occurs. In the upper image, the distribution of muscles spindles are found around the areas where dense structures are, like intermuscular septa, light grey in the lower image.

tract (muscle-fascia path, see Figure 4). In other words, movement of body parts could arise from forces acting both: (a) in an inner osseous endoskeleton, through muscle-tendon-bone attachments, and (b) in a fibrous skeleton, through muscle-fascia attachments and fascia-fascia expansions. Multiple force-transmission paths would be an important feature to the force *distribution* within the fascial system.

Most musculoskeletal pain syndromes are related to *mechanical overload* of moving tissues, often resulting from force *concentrated* in certain areas (for instance, the entheses). Hence, the more the forces are *distributed*, the less the likelihood of tissue overload to arise. One can then visualize Rolfing interventions and related manual approaches that can affect/optimize myofascial force transmission within these two co-acting skeletons contributing to higher

movement quality and amelioration of symptoms related to tissue overload, damage, and inflammation.

7. Mechanoreception and Proprioception

Standard classification of mechano–receptors divides them into joint receptors for somatesthesia, kinesthesia, and muscle receptors for muscle motor control. Joint receptors are present in capsules and ligaments; muscle receptors are present in muscles and tendons.

Again, anatomical classification seems to impart a broader understanding of how the whole works. The classification of proprioceptors as either 'muscle receptors' or 'joint receptors' seems to be artificially based on the anatomical distinction between ligaments and muscles as passive and active structures,

respectively, as discussed above. Considering the *continuity* of connective-tissue structures that seem to include ligaments, capsules, tendons, and fascia, van der Wal reported to us during the FRSS the distribution of receptors in the forearm of rats, specifically the distribution of proprioceptive receptors, follows a functional logic rather than an anatomical one.

He detected that the distribution of mechanoreceptors was not homogenous within myofascial structures, but rather they were present mainly in the regions where there is a *deformation* of tissue when subjected to mechanical stresses (see Figure 5). Dense connective tissue, which deforms very little under stress, showed no mechanoreceptors. In the *transition* between dense connective structures, muscle fibers, and areolar connective tissue, all deformable interfaces, those receptors were present. What's more, the distinction between joint and muscle receptors seemed not to make sense. The features of the receptors found were described as being both joint *and* muscle receptors. In other words, the distribution of proprioceptive receptors seemed to follow the *functional architecture* of the connective tissue and not its location (e.g., ligaments/muscles), as they are commonly described.

The presence of both receptors where tissues of different mechanical properties meet, i.e., in areas that undergo *deformation* when under stress, showed how the deformation is the condition that makes them able to convey information about mechanical stresses to the CNS. Different kinds of receptors are located where mechanical stresses can be sensed/measured in a continuous in-series chain of structures that encompasses bone-fascia-muscle-fascia-bone, defying the historical classification of proprioceptors.

8. Dynamic Ligaments: Dynaments

In so being, one can conceive joint stabilization function as being accomplished by continuous soft-tissue structures linking bone-to-bone, the constitution of which depends on their *functional* demands. The amount and type of tissue (muscle and fascia) between bones will correspond to the relative movement of these segments as they link together. This collection of associated tissues will vary from more fibrous or less fibrous, to more muscular or less muscular. This is the 'dynament'

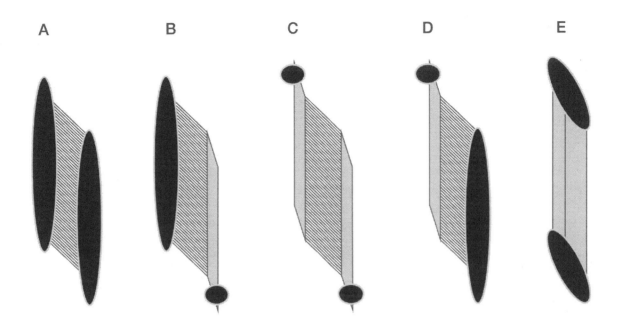

A   B   C   D   E

Figure 6: The dynament concept. [Note: superior aspects of shapes are proximal and inferior aspects of shapes are distal.] (A) Long oval black shapes are bones. This is a 'pure' muscle where the angled stripes are the muscle bellies within their connective-tissue scaffolding. (B) Proximal bone continuous with muscle tissue, distally inserting into regular dense connective-tissue structures – a tendon. (C) Muscle fascicles span between two regular dense connective-tissue structures. (D) Proximal regular dense connective-tissue structure, where muscle tissue spans to the skeletal element (periosteum). (E) No musle tissue intermediating, only regular dense connective tissue – a 'pure' ligament (van der Wal 2009). There would be no distinction between 'muscle', 'tendon', 'ligament', being that all of them are part of a functional continuum aimed at dynamically linking bones.

model put forth by van der Wal back in the 1980s, that brings in a renewed principle of functional units underlying motor control. According to this vision, what has been described as ligaments, tendons, and muscles can all be unified as dynamic ligaments, or *dynaments* constituted by in-series organization of soft tissue (fascia and muscle fibers) between bones (see Figure 6). One dynament may show no muscle fibers and be considered a pure 'ligament' like the cruciate ligaments of the knee and interosseous membranes. On the other side of the spectrum, a dynament can have almost exclusively muscle fibers like the deltoid, and all the possibilities of more or less fibrous tissue (tendons, aponeuroses) interposed in between. So, the functional units of motor action can be considered the dynament units, where the CNS is orchestrating their function in a task-oriented manner.

Walshe (1946) cited the physiologist John Huglings Jackson (1835-1911), who had already said, back in the 1890s, to paraphrase, that the CNS knows nothing about muscles but about *movements* of muscles. Van der Wal recalls and reviews

this notion with the lens of connective-tissue architecture and distribution of proprioceptors. There is not a 'map' of muscles in the CNS, rather it is sensitive to changes in mechanical information conveyed by proprioception. Changes in relationships of body parts during posture and movement will deform the connective-tissue structures involved, which will change the proprioceptive afferents entering the CNS. Such information processed and integrated with the organism's action plan will eventually produce muscle activity accordingly; by its turn, it will give continuous feedback to the proprioceptive afferents. This is a loop where proprioceptive information will reenter the CNS and give rise to the appropriate motor control efferents to accomplish the plan in a real-time, continuous servomechanism. The CNS continuously compares actions, plans, and execution while making the appropriate adjustments.

9. Manual Therapy and Proprioception

Now you can see, actual anatomy is much more than those clean structures shown

in anatomy drawings. There is continuity of the whole connective-tissue system. As Rolfers, we work with the possibility that fascia-oriented manual input can change the amount or balance between connection/disconnection among moving structures. It is possible to take our intervention further to visualize that it would be possible to change the quality of proprioceptive information entering the CNS with the therapeutic touch acting on these dynament units. If connective-tissue structures have plasticity, then manual therapists can influence the amount and the location of connection/disconnection of parts. This could change the mechanical environment where proprioceptors are embedded, possibly bringing them towards their *optimal range* of proprioceptive function. Tension receptors are known to work best under a certain degree of tensile stress. Too much or too little tension would hamper mechanoreceptors' functions. By changing the relationship between connection/disconnection of parts towards a more homogeneous distribution of basal tension, fascia-oriented manipulation input could optimize the quality of the neural afferents from mechanoreceptors to the CNS. By lowering the strain in areas already subjected to a habitually high degree of tension and, at the same time, redirecting forces to areas previously under lower tension, appropriate hands-on work could help the *distribution* of tensile stress in the connective-tissue web. This effect would correspond to better mechanoreceptive afferent signaling, which, by its turn, could potentially reflect in higher movement quality.

10. Studying Organisms' Integrity: Tensegrity?

Rather than the body being a collection of parts, connective tissue establishes *relationships* among parts. It follows that if one wants to understand the systemic functions of an organism, i.e., the relationship of its parts, one should somehow integrate the study of anatomy with the study of the *integrity*. In this context, van der Wal mentioned the concept of *tensegrity* as a possible means to understand better how the whole human works. The tensegrity principle was found in many presentations at the FRSS and was also the subject of a workshop presented by Danièle-Claude Martin.

Tensegrity systems are built by compression-bearing elements 'floating' in a pre-tensioned web of tension-bearing elements. The tension within such systems is evenly distributed so that it *integrates* all parts of the system. If one part moves, the whole system immediately changes and adapts to that movement. In a tensegrity system, all parts are interconnected. If the distribution of tension within the web is uneven, then the interconnectedness of its parts will diminish (we could recall here Ida Rolf, PhD, using the illustration of tents). Some of its parts will be under too much tension and others under too little tension, hampering the assembly of the system and its function. The same idea could be applied to human bodies, which should maintain tensegrity during movement. That is to say, the system should be able to adapt and maintain an appropriate distribution of tension while changing body configurations to maintain the internal connectedness that characterizes tensegrity.

For instance, flexing the torso by simply bending the thorax in the direction of the pelvis, loosening tension in the belly (as in a 'slouched' posture), we lose the tensional integration and hence its role in maintaining the support of the trunk. This situation would probably be associated with poor overall force distribution and likely to lead to tissue overload – potential tissue damage. This would likely lead to inflammation and pain. But if, in flexing the torso, an appropriate degree of tension is also present in the belly (the concave side), tensegrity would be maintained, rendering better trunk support and a more homogenous force distribution in the system, a better movement pattern.

11. Neural and Non-Neural Connectivity within Live Tensegrity Structures

So, the distribution of tension is a key aspect in tensegrity structures, and it is a condition to maintain the integration of its interconnected parts. What's more, such integration may be conceived as having two main control sources. One, and the more obvious, is *neural*, as discussed above. The quality of proprioception can be reflected in the integration of the person's movement, an effect mediated by the CNS. Two, more recent research shows that there may be an additional integrative control mechanism that does not involve the CNS directly and resides in the structure itself. This second integrative control is *non-neural*, and is a distinctive feature of tensegrity structures. These structures behave in a fashion in which morphology, physical forces, and displacements act as non-neural channels of information generation and communication, the so-called *morphological communication* (Rieffel et al. 2010). This mechanism is based on the tensile forces within the continuous pre-tensioned web of the tensegrity structure. Under tensegrity, local structure configuration changes affect the tensile forces within the whole structure in a purely mechanical action. Such communication takes place at the speed of sound, faster than neural mechanisms.

Think of the variations and discontinuities in the distribution of tensile forces in the connective-tissue web, what would hamper its *structural* connectivity as well as its *neural* connectivity (through the lack of morphological and neural communication respectively)? Both mechanisms may interrupt whole-body tensegrity and high-quality movement. So, the original continuity and communicability of the connective-tissue web may exhibit, depending on the arrangement of its parts, higher or lower degrees of tensile integrity, or tensegrity. As manual therapists, we may help the distribution of tensile stresses in our clients' systems by changing, among additional variables, the mechanical loading along with myofascial structures and consequently the net baseline tension in the connective tissue web.

In short, a better distribution of tension may have the effect of enhancing movement quality: (a) via neural control, by improving the mechanosensitive input and hence offer the CNS better conditions to control movement; (b) via

Actual anatomy is much more than those clean structures shown in anatomy drawings. There is continuity of the whole connective tissue system. As Rolfers, we work with the possibility that fascia-oriented manual input can change the amount or balance between connection/disconnection among moving structures.

ameliorating the degree of morphological communication among its parts. The latter is an effect that may enhance non-neural mechanisms of motor control, related to tensegrity. Interestingly, pandiculation (yawning and morning stretching) seems to be a natural and inherited way to achieve such effects. Through creating tensegrity in various positions, pandiculation updates maximum bodily dimensions, these actions seem to autoregulate myofascial connection/ disconnection balance, refreshing the baseline tension distribution. This, in turn, stimulates morphological and neural communication, and maintains the quality of movement. Pandiculation could then be conceived as a sort of myofascial hygiene (Bertolucci 2011).

12. Alternative Methodologies to Study Fascia?

The above descriptions show the difficulty of studying fascia. Anatomists do a fair amount of cutting to show us specific structures, yet we know fascia has an integrative function, easily disrupted by the current analytic methods.

An additional example of this difficulty was presented at the FRSS by Freddy Sichting, PhD, describing the so-called heel-pad paradox, which refers to differences in stiffness of the heel pad measured *in vitro* compared to *in vivo* (Pain and Challis 2001). *In vitro* stiffness appears to be much greater than *in vivo* but a conclusive explanation is still missing. Nonetheless, the studies that led to such a paradox were based on current deterministic and reductionist scientific methods calculating the mean values of variables to establish what is 'normal'. It is possible that such methods are not appropriate due to the complexity and individuality of fascia development, remodeling, and behavior.

In his presentation, Sichting relayed an analogy: "Connective tissue is a poem of which we are still trying to understand the letters" and he questioned whether we should question and possibly revise the methods used so far. As an alternative, he mentions the possibility of studying each individual and trying to learn from each one. Interestingly such a view matches Rolf's distinction between normal and median: she would say that 'normal' refers to the full potential of each individual, and mean (what in academia is typically related to 'normal') is average for the whole population, which is less than what nature could achieve.

Conclusion

Modern science has evolved trying to isolate, as much as possible, the various aspects of a phenomenon and study one part at a time. Such a method is well suited for many fields, but not so much for researching fascia, as connective tissue has a role of integrating the functions of all systems and hence exhibits an extremely complex behavior. This makes fascia very difficult to isolate its roles. Does fascia deserve alternative methodologies so we can have a comprehensive understanding of its many functions? More recent methodologies aimed to study *complex systems* are being put forward. They deal with connectivity and emergent properties (Turnbull et al. 2018) which may also be useful in the fascia research field.

Luiz Fernando Bertolucci, MD, MSc, is a faculty member of the Brazilian Rolfing® Association where he teaches anatomy and myofascial release. He is also a biologist and a physician who specialized in physiatry (rehabilitation) and has been applying Rolfing SI in the treatment of musculoskeletal disorders since 1990.

He discovered a new style of touch (Tensegrity Touch), which he teaches worldwide and researches

Author's note: I wish to deeply thank Lina Amy Hack, BS, BA, Advanced Rolfer, for her comprehensive effort to read, comment, add, and edit this article.

References

Bertolucci, L. F. 2011. Pandiculation: Nature's way of maintaining the functional integrity of the myofascial system? *Journal of Bodywork and Movement Therapies* 15(3):268-280.

Huijing, P. A., H. Maas, and G. C. Baan. 2003. Compartmental fasciotomy and isolating a muscle from neighboring muscles interfere with myofascial force transmission within the rat anterior crural compartment. *Journal of Morphology* 256(3):306-21.

Jobe, C. M. and M. J. Coen. 2004. Gross anatomy of the shoulder. In *The Shoulder, third edition*, eds F. A. Matsen, M. A. Wirth, and S. B. Lippitt, xx-xx. Philadelphia:Saunders.

Pain, M. T., and J. H. Challis. 2001. The role of the heel pad and shank soft tissue during impacts: A further resolution of a paradox. *Journal of Biomechanics* 34(3):327-33.

Rieffel, J. A., F. J. Valero-Cuevas, and H. Lipson. 2010. Morphological communication: Exploiting coupled dynamics in a complex mechanical structure to achieve locomotion. *Journal of the Royal Society Interface* 7:613-621.

Stecco, C. 2015. *Functional atlas of the human fascial system*. New York, NY: Elsevier.

Testut, L. 1904. *Traité d'anatomie humaine*. Paris, France: Doin.

In vitro stiffness appears to be much greater than *in vivo* but a conclusive explanation is still missing. Nonetheless, the studies that led to such a paradox were based on current deterministic and reductionist scientific methods calculating the mean values of variables to establish what is 'normal'.

Modern science has evolved trying to isolate, as much as possible, the various aspects of a phenomenon and study one part at a time. Such a method is suited for many fields, but not so much to research fascia, as connective tissue has a role of integrating functions of all systems and hence exhibits an extremely complex behavior.

Turnbull, L., M.-T. Hütt, A. A. Ioannides, S. Kininmonth, R. Poeppl, K. Tockner, L. J. Bracken, S. Keesstra, L. Liu, R. Masselink, and A. J. Parsons. 2018. Connectivity and complex systems: Learning from a multi-disciplinary perspective. *Applied Network Science* 3(1):1-49.

van der Wal, J. 2009. The architechture of the connective tissue in the musculoskeletal system – An often overlooked functional parameter as to proprioception in the locomotor apparatus. *International Journal of Therapeutic Massage & Bodywork* 2(4):9-23.

van der Wal, J. 2020. Fascia, fabrica or fabric – On the origin of fascia. Available from https://www.embryo.nl

Walshe, F. M. R. 1946. *On the contribution of clinical study to the physiology of the cerebral cortex: The Victor Horsley memorial lecture,* 18. Edinburgh: E&S Livingstone Ltd. As cited by: Bobath B. 1978. Atividade Postural Reflexa Anormal Causada por Lesões Cerebrais, 2a Edição. Ed. Manole Ltda. São Paulo.

Fascial Recoil

Wiley Patterson, MD, Certified Advanced Rolfer®,
and Rolf Movement® Practitioner

Wiley Patterson

ABSTRACT *This article discusses some basic mechanical properties of fascia, including its elastic properties and their significance to structural integration gleaned from the 2016 Fascia Research Summer School held in Leipzig, Germany.*

International Fascia Conference

A Fascia Research Summer School (FRSS) was held in Leipzig, Germany, in September 2016, with Robert Schleip, PhD, and Thomas Findley, MD, instrumental in organizing these ongoing conferences. Schleip has been a Rolfer for decades and earned a PhD in human biology where he focused on fascial studies, and he has become a potent voice and liaison for Rolfing® Structural Integration's (SI) interaction with mainstream lines of fascial inquiry. Findley was a world-class leader of fascial research and academic communities who have amplified and validated the clinical work of Rolfing SI for decades. As a result

of their work, more and more fascial research articles written each year. This particular conference attracted presenters and attendees from dozens of countries. Besides Rolfing SI practitioners, professionals from physical rehabilitation, pain management, orthopedics, athletic performance, massage, anatomy, acupuncture, and histological fascial research were well represented. Some of the notable structural integration presenters included Tom Meyers, former Rolfer and the developer Kinesis Myofascial Integration of structural bodywork from Maine; Fernando Bertolucci, MD, physician and Rolfer from Brazil; and the aforementioned Robert Schleip, PhD, Rolfer, and Feldenkrais® practitioner from Germany.

Personally, I had two favorite presentations: Gunnar Spohr, DO, MD, who presented fascial recoil in his presentation titled "The heart as a fascial organ" and Bertolucci's "Tensegrity touch." The ideas about facial recoil intrigued me greatly and this article is devoted to summarizing some of the main points Spohr presented at the conference. I want to mention to you, the SI community, "Tensegrity touch" was quite pertinent to my Rolfing practice and I was able to immediately put Bertolucci's presented suggestions into action. I had never viewed working with the 'sleeve' of the body in this way before. He keeps his attention and intervention in the superficial fascia and truly profound changes occur. This topic will not be covered in this article, though I highly recommend his training on this technique. As I mentioned, this discussion is inspired by Spohr and his presentation "The heart as a fascial organ."

Fascial Elasticity

Elasticity is the ability of a material to regain its original shape after distortion. Another common use of the word elastic is 'stretchiness' as in the stretchy band of one's underwear. However, the first definition is of more importance to this discussion regarding the biophysics of fascia. Imagine three spheres of equal dimension, one made of marshmallow, one of rubber, and the last one of stainless steel. Drop each sphere onto the hard, level surface of a steel anvil and observe how high each sphere bounces. The marshmallow will splat and barely bounce. The rubber ball will bounce quite a bit, but the stainless-steel ball will bounce highest. It has the greatest capacity to regain its original shape. The energy imparted into the marshmallow ball is lost on impact, spread throughout the weak internal organization. The stainless-steel ball has a much higher level of molecular crystalline (not glass) organization and has better resistance to chaotic, disorganized transfer of energy. The potential energy converting to kinetic energy on impact is conserved best by the stainless-steel ball by not changing the shape of the object, the energy of the impact is sent through the stainless-steel ball with minimal distortion of its shape and the ball is lifted highest away from the anvil.

Most of us have seen slow-motion videos of a golf ball being compressed and regaining its shape after the golf club head impact. It is this force that is involved in regaining its original shape that imparts much of the eventual distance. If you hit a marshmallow with the same force and speed, the distance it travels is minimal. This reminds me of a video I saw of the tibial distortion of a gymnast landing from a vault. The bone looks as if it will certainly explode from the marked distortion, but it doesn't, and the gymnast bounces upward as the stored force normalizes. Imagine a slingshot. As one pulls the sling back, stretching the elastic bands, potential energy is imparted into and stored in the elastics (see Figure 1). It does not matter how fast nor how slowly the elastics are stretched, only how far. The force imparted into the dimension of the distortion from its original shape determines the amount of energy stored into the sling shot. As the sling is released and the elastics shorten, the projectile is hurled forward. Its speed and distance depend on the ratio of the potential energy stored in the elastics relative to the projectile's mass. A BB will fly farther than a golf ball given equal pulls from the same slingshot.

The working unit of a skeletal muscle, a sarcomere, is composed of actin-myosin myofilaments. During contraction, the myosin 'ratchets' the actin inward, the sarcomere shortens and pulls its Z-lines toward each other, thereby shortening the sarcomere. The attached bone, via the tendon, will be moved. However, by pre-stretching a muscle-tendon-fascial plane arrangement, more force can be generated than by mere muscle contraction alone. It is estimated that elastic recoil can add as much as 40% to the inherent muscular force of any movement.

Fascia is highly elastic and this property defines much of its function. Healthy fascia resists stretching and tends to regain its original shape. For example, the coach of a gold-medal sprinter at the Rio de Janeiro Olympics, in his "Teach Me to Run" video course, emphasizes the need

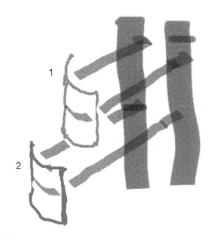

Figure 1: Slingshot in both slack position (1) and activated position (2), ready to fire once activated.

to dorsiflex the ankle and toes on each stride. This lengthens the plantar fascia and Achilles tendon, stretching them and increasing potential energy. I tested the idea. Walking on a sidewalk, I noticed a stranger ahead of me, walking at the same speed. I neither gained nor lost ground as we walked. I then decided to gently but completely dorsiflex my toes and ankles with each forward swing of my calves. I very quickly passed the person. I felt the stretch-generated tension and the extra force available as I pushed off. My stride lengthened from the extra force without a conscious effort to lengthen my stride nor to work harder. The same coach also asks his sprinters to raise their knees high during each forward stride, stretching the gluteal and hamstring fascia. So, if you experiment with high knees, dorsiflexed ankles, and dorsiflexed toes while sprinting, you will feel this effect on your fascia and subsequent increase in speed.

Fascial Recoil in the Heart and Blood Vessels

Another fascinating example is the concept of fascial recoil in cardiac and vascular function. In Figure 2, you will notice that all four heart valves are

Fascia is highly elastic and this property defines much of its function. Healthy fascia resists stretching and tends to regain its original shape.

Fascial recoil is a basic principle in the functional nature of fascia and is highly involved in the conservation of energy in the continuity of movement, but also in the basic function of rhythmic movements such as peristalsis, breathing, and craniosacral rhythms.

close to each other and lie mostly on the same plane. Let us consider just the left ventricle, the aortic valve, and the ascending aorta. As systole occurs, the left ventricle contracts and pushes blood through the aortic valve into the ascending aorta. As the heart contracts, the valve plane moves downward away from the aortic arch about a centimeter. As the blood from the left ventricle enters the ascending aorta, the circumferential connective-tissue layers comprising the aorta are distended. Both the heart valve plane movement and the aortic widening are fascial distensions and thereby have stored potential energy. As the ventricular contraction ends, the unidirectional aortic valve shuts and then is passively moved back upward to its previous position. As it shuts, and is moved distally, the closed valve face slingshots the left ventricular blood, now in the ascending aorta, further along the aorta. The stretched fascia of the myocardial wall wants to elastically regain its original shape.

The bolus of blood leaving the left ventricle widens the diameter of the aorta which is then subject to another fascial recoil in a self-perpetuating passive peristaltic movement along the course of the artery. So, the left ventricular contraction moves blood out of the left ventricle into the ascending aorta, but that blood needs the fascial recoil inherent in the structure of the arterial system to move it all the way down to the feet. The heart itself has a spiraling fascial organization to help conserve energy. Fascial recoil is part of the motor of the heart. The muscular contractions activate the slingshot-like fascial recoil. The heart works as a dynament (omnidirectional – no origin nor insertion; see Figure 3). Dynament is a term coined by Jaap van der Wal, MD, PhD, which is the idea of architectural units of connection and force transmission in the posture and locomotion system (2020). [See Bertolucci's article, page 56 to 65, for more information about van der Wal's dynament concept.] Therefore, its contractions mainly work on these fascial

arrangements. The cardiac muscle of the left ventricle does not pump through the vasculature, instead it primes the aorta (just like the left atrium primes the left ventricle) and activates the fascial recoil of the valve plane and arterial walls.

The following link shows the heart valve plane movement and other systolic distortions:

https://bit.ly/3KS8Lrm

Fascial Recoil in Movement

The contralateral nature of walking is a good example of storing potential energy and releasing it as kinetic energy through fascial recoil. Fascial recoil is a basic principle in the functional nature of fascia and is highly involved in the conservation of energy in the continuity of movement, but also in the basic function of rhythmic movements such as peristalsis, breathing, and craniosacral rhythms. In Figure 4, the stored potential energy visible in this

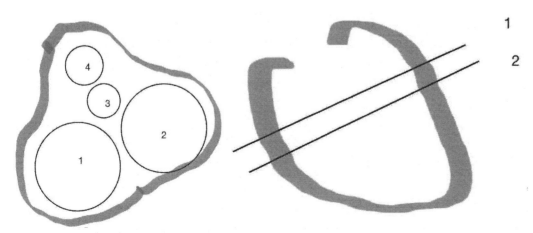

Figure 2: Diagramatic horizontal section showing the valve plane of the heart (1. bicuspid valve; 2. tricuspid valve; 3. aortic valve; 4. pulmonary valve).

Figure 3: Diagrammatic sagittal section of the fascial architecture of the heart as a dynament (postion 1 is the valve plane during diastole with the plane moving to position 2 during systole).

Figure 4: The stored potential energy is visible in this young hiker's contralateral coordination which is storing potential energy to aid the next step forward. Photo courtesy of the author.

Figure 5: Fascial recoil will allow this dancer to return to an erect posture. Photo courtesy of the author.

young hiker's contralateral coordination is waiting to aid the next forward step. The potential energy is stored in the structure of the fascial system itself and is released as kinetic energy in moving forward.

In Figure 5, the dancer has stored potential energy in the fascia of her rectus abdominis, iliopsoas, and other hip flexors. It is obvious that she cannot stay in this position for long. She will straighten her torso and hips mainly from fascial recoil rather than contraction of the iliopsoas and assisting hip flexors.

This stored potential energy also aids in longevity, as suggested by a study of older men doing hopping training (Hoffren-Mikkola et al. 2015). Over eleven weeks, there were verifiable improvements in strength and balance in this group. This came about due to an increase in fascial recoil. As we age, the physical qualities of our fascia change and we lose some fascial recoil. How many sixty-plus-year-old people do you know who would want to jump down from a four-foot height? At twenty years old, this can easily be done, yet it becomes unappealing or even scary as we reach our senior years. However, fascial recoil can be improved using Wolf's law – connective tissue restructures itself according to the forces acting upon it.

So, skipping, jogging, or bouncing on a trampoline will increase the amount of fascial recoil. A slight vibration to the impact on the fascia is necessary to increase its elasticity. Speed also seems to help in this restructuring of the fascia.

Along those lines, a study by Gale et al. (2007) looked at grip strength in the elderly as a predictor of mortality rates. Grip strength can be improved by muscular use and it gives a pertinent assessment of fascial competency in functioning. Improvement in fascial competency, due to an increase in grip strength, lessened deaths from cardiovascular disease and cancer in the test subjects.

Conclusion

This discussion of fascial recoil covers the basic properties of elastic recoil inherent in fascia, as presented by Spohr at the 2016 FRSS. It shows its power and primary importance in human organization relative to gravity and in basic principles of movement. Healthy fascial recoil is also a predictor of vitality, aging, and mortality.

Wiley Patterson, MD, graduated from medical school in 1978 and has been a Certified Rolfer since 1992. He completed his Advanced Rolfing training in 1999, Rolf Movement® training in 2008 and Somatic Experiencing® training in 2018. He began studying osteopathy in 1999 and continues attending osteopathic classes. He started the Austin Structural Integration Study Group that has been meeting in Austin, Texas, for the past six years. He has organized classes and conferences for the Red River Region of the Dr. Ida Rolf Institute®.

References

Gale, C.R., C.N. Martyn, C. Cooper and A.A. Sayer. 2007. Grip strength, body composition, and mortality. *International Journal of Epidemilogy* 36(1):228-235.

Hoffren-Mikkola, M., M. Ishikawa, T. Rantalainen, J. Avela and P.V. Komi. 2015. Neuromuscular mechanics and hopping training in the elderly. *European Journal of Applied Physiology* 115:863-877.

van der Wal, J. 2020. *Fascia, fabrica or fabric: On the origin of fascia.* Available at https://bit.ly/3JErZ1X

Perspectives on Inflammation

By Jeffrey Burch, Certified Advanced Rolfer®

Jeffrey Burch

ABSTRACT *This article describes inflammation, what it is, what it is not, how to recognize when it is a valuable part of healing, and when it may be an impediment to healing. Emphasis is given to finding the source(s) of inflammation as a key to healing.*

In our practices clients often arrive describing inflammation in their bodies. Sometimes there are objective signs related to these client perceptions that we can observe, sometimes not. Sometimes we see signs of inflammation that a client may not have mentioned. These situations are highly variable and sometimes challenging to assess. Here is some of what I have gathered about inflammation over the decades. I am eager for what others will add.

We each experience inflammation from time to time in our bodies. Our clients often present with inflammation. Inflammation can be focal or generalized in the body. As common as inflammation is, it is not fully understood in the medical research world and remains an active area of research. Given the complexity of inflammation and the incomplete state of our knowledge, it is easy to see why there are frequent misunderstandings and disagreements about what inflammation is and how to manage it.

In this article there are three takeaways:

- Not all inflammation is bad; sometimes it is a very good thing. Learn to recognize the difference. Act accordingly.

- Inflammation is a symptom, actually called a 'sign', which is an outward manifestation. A symptom is the patient's reaction to that phenomenon, not a cause. While it is sometimes appropriate to act directly to control inflammation as a first-line action, always look for the sources of the inflammation.

- Do not conflate inflammation and pain. They are not the same thing. They may or may not occur together.

On a micro level, inflamed tissue involves important changes in biochemistry and the accumulation of certain migratory cell types. It is worth studying up on these inflammatory mechanisms. This kind of knowledge about inflammation fills books and is not the focus of this article. On a macro level, inflammation is marked by extra fluid and warmth in an area. Inflammation is often but not always accompanied by pain or discomfort. The subject of this article is recognizing the signs of inflammation, how observations and client history can direct our thinking and strategy for intervention.

Probe what your clients tell you. Clients will often say they have inflammation when what they actually feel is pain. There may or may not be pain associated with mild to moderate inflammation. Conversely, pain is frequently felt where there is no inflammation. If there is no edema and no extra warmth, either there is no inflammation, or it is too deep or diffuse to be outwardly manifested. This is also an opportunity to educate clients.

Physiology of Inflammation

In response to injury or infection, there are many biochemicals of the inflammatory response, so called inflammatory mediators, such as the complement system, cytokines, interleukins, and superoxides. These immunoregulatory proteins are released at the injury or infection site as a reaction to the damaged tissue, injury or infection will cause capillaries in the area to leak fluids. This also will damage cells because of disruption to the sodium, calcium, and potassium pumping mechanisms of the local cells, this in turn will cause swelling within the damaged cells. As the damage is repaired, some ruptured tissue is liquified and carried off by the lymphatic vessels, eventually destined to return back to the blood stream and to the liver where it is recycled. Certain white blood cells, like polymorphonuclear cells and monocytes are phagocytic, in other words these cells sort of eat up and carry away debris to the liver and the spleen for recycling. As the damaged tissue is removed and the inflamed cells begin to function properly, the cells are able to again restore the balance of ions such as sodium, calcium, and potassium. This shifts the edema back to the extracellular environment; the excess fluid will move through the lymph to the bloodstream and swelling is abated.

Inflammatory mediators bring more fluids to the area as an essential early step in the body's healing response. With this fluid filling a local region, we observe swelling or edema, and an increase in warmth. Such inflammation in response

Not all inflammation is bad; sometimes it is a very good thing. Learn to recognize the difference. Act accordingly.

to injury or infection is not an enemy to be controlled, it is a friend. Up to a point, inflammation in response to injured tissue is a highly useful step in healing. However, inflammation in response to acute injury or infection can be excessive, in which case it may be useful to reduce but not eliminate the inflammation. There is a grey area of how much inflammation is enough, and leads to the question: when does swelling become pathological? If there has been a recent insult to an area and some inflammation is present, it may be better to take no direct action against the inflammation or to use only the mildest measures such as elevating the body part. If the tissue is very swollen and red, inflammation may be greater than is useful for healing. In this situation, judicious use of the PRICE protocol (protection, rest, ice, compression, and elevation) may be useful. When excessive inflammation in response to injury is seen, infection should be ruled out.

What to Do With Inflammation

Allopathic medicine typically recommends steroids and nonsteroidal anti-inflammatory medications for treatment of inflammation and injury. Nonsteroidal agents (NSAIDs) include aspirin, ibuprofen, and aleve. The steroidal anti-inflammatory medications such as prednisone, cortisone, and methylprednisolone are all variants of the cortisone molecule. Both steroids and NSAIDs may reduce edema, heat, and pain, but at a cost. They can be necessary and useful to abate severe inflammation to the point where normal processes will allow healing, but may slow or, in high doses, stop tissue healing. Even the application of an ice pack may slow tissue healing, but is useful in reducing the excessive inflammation that can occur within the first days after an injury. All NSAID medications, in high doses or for a protracted time, can be hard on the liver and kidneys. These medications may also lead to digestive-system bleeding.

Chronic inflammation requires a different perspective. Causes of acute inflammation are easy enough to identify. But chronic inflammation – inflammation that persists

after a wound is healed or which arises absent of injury and remains for more than a few weeks – can seem to create a feedback loop wherein inflammation becomes self-perpetuating. In chronic inflammation there is also usually a cause or several causes driving the inflammation, the presence of inflammation seems as if an injury has occurred, causing the release of damaged tissue. In this case of chronic swelling the cause(s) could be disruption from the outside (blows, abrasions, or cuts), could be tissue damage inside from repetitive strain, could be acute strain, or there could also be toxic exposures that may be focal. For example, contact with a noxious plant or a spider sting. There are also generalized toxic exposures, which may be inhaled or ingested, but that affect some local tissues more than others. Chronic inflammation can be when the immune response creates more cell damage, it can also become a positive feedback mechanism where the initial swelling causes even more of an inflammatory response. This is an example of an instance when corticosteroids and more advanced drugs may be needed to break the immune response cycle and calm the reaction down. It is imperative to search for these causes. This isn't always easy. Remove the cause(s) and the inflammation will diminish. Often, inflammation of a more generalized type in the blood vessels has been shown to increase the possibilities of damage to organs, including the lungs, heart, and brain.

There are many possible causes of inflammation:

- Chronic exposure to irritating substances is common. Frequent culprits are food sensitivities and airborne irritants, including mold or chemicals.

- Laundry products and other cleaning agents can be important contributors to inflammation, usually to the skin and mucous membranes.

- Pet sensitivities are a common and unfortunate source, which usually manifests with inflammation of the eyes, nose, and sinus, and/or lungs in the form of asthma.

In chronic inflammation there is also usually a cause or several causes driving the inflammation . . . It is imperative to search for these causes. This isn't always easy. Remove the cause(s) and the inflammation will diminish.

- Movement habits and other body use patterns frequently drive inflammation, often to joints, muscles, ligaments, tendons, and to and around bony tissue.
- About 20% of the population has some form of sleep apnea-related disorder which frequently leads to tissue damage in many parts of the body.[1]

There is commonly more than one cause of inflammation. Don't stop when the first irritant is found. 'Search satisfaction' is a bias practitioners need to monitor for, it means – finding something related to the problem under investigation and assuming it is the whole story – it is a common error, don't stop investigating after the first source of inflammation is detected. It may not even be one of the larger contributors to the problem. No matter how much you find, keep looking.

Inflammation is a *sign* leading to *symptom(s)*; it is not a *cause*. Find the *source(s)*. If the source is not removed, our attempts to control inflammation are akin to trying to smother a fire fed and fanned from another direction. This sort of cross controlling will not eliminate the problem and can easily lead to new problems.

It is worth noting that when there is inflammation in response to an identifiable injury, there may also be undiagnosed chronic inflammation. The injury can then result in excessive inflammation. When presented with an injury or infection, it is important to look for signs of chronic systemic inflammation that may have preexisted the acute event.

Protocols with the acronyms PRICE and MEAT offer good first-line treatment for inflammation.

PRICE

- Protection
- Rest
- Ice
- Compression
- Elevation

MEAT

- Movement
- Exercise
- Analgesia
- Treatment

Treatment for the MEAT protocol can include joint mobilization, acupuncture, soft-tissue release, laser, ice, heat, TENS, etc. The MEAT protocol is more recent than the PRICE protocol and is sometimes presented as an 'upgrade' from PRICE. My impression is that there is a place for both. PRICE may be more appropriate early in the healing process, particularly for more severe injuries. MEAT may be more appropriate a little later in the healing process, for less severe injuries, and certainly for noninjury related inflammation and/or pain. Elements of both PRICE and MEAT can be used in the same time period for the same condition.

As always, if what you are doing isn't working, try something else. If you are not having success or are otherwise in doubt, consult with colleagues and/or refer.

Endnote

1. The general term is sleep disordered breathing (SDB), which includes obstructive sleep apnea, central sleep apnea, upper airway resistance syndrome, and obesity hypoventilation. In these apnea and apnea-like conditions, during the night, much of the body is deprived of oxygen, and even blood flow, many times per hour. The person is also partially awakening several times per hour and rarely, if ever, getting into the deepest restorative levels of sleep. This is damaging and can lead to somnolescence during the day, increased blood pressures in the lungs, which stresses the right-sided chambers of the heart, and can lead to arrhythmias like atrial fibrillation, increasing the risk of stroke, heart attack, and sudden death. While up to twenty percent of the population of the United States, Canada, and Europe has one of these sleep disorders, they may also,

as a result, live with chronic fatigue and also have a higher incidence of chronic pain. Learn all the subtle signs of sleep disordered breathing and screen all clients for it in my earlier article (Burch 2020). In my practice I detect an average of one or more clients per month with sleep apnea. Proper treatment of the sleep breathing disorder reduces or eliminates many health complaints. Depending on the form of sleep disordered breathing and the rest of the person's health picture, treatment can take many forms including speech therapy, surgery, or a CPAP machine. Manual therapy alone is rarely enough.

Jeffrey Burch received bachelor's degrees in biology and psychology, and a master's degree in counseling from the University of Oregon. He was certified as a Rolfer® in 1977 and completed his advanced Rolfing® Structural Integration certification in 1990. Burch studied cranial manipulation in three different schools, including with French osteopath Alain Gehin. Starting in 1998 he began studying visceral manipulation with Jean-Pierre Barral and his associates, completing the apprenticeship to teach visceral manipulation. Although no longer associated with the Barral Institute, Burch has Barral's permission to teach visceral manipulation. Having learned assessment and treatment methods in several osteopathically-derived schools, he then developed several new assessment and treatment methods that he now teaches, along with established methods. In recent years he has developed original methods for assessing and releasing fibrosities in joint capsules, bursas, and tendon sheathes, which he is also beginning to teach. Burch is the founding editor of the IASI Yearbook *to which he contributes regularly, as well as to other journals. For more information visit www.jeffreyburch.com.*

Reference

Burch, Jeffrey. 2020. Assessing for sleep-disordered breathing. *Structure, Function, Integration* 48(2):47-54.

The Path of an Advanced Rolfing® Instructor

An Interview with Pierpaola Volpones

By John Schewe, Basic Rolfing Instructor, and Pierpaola Volpones, Advanced Rolfing Instructor

John Schewe

Pierpaola Volpones

ABSTRACT *This conversation between two Dr. Ida Rolf Institute® (DIRI) faculty members focus on the path Pierpaola Volpones has traveled to becoming a Rolf Movement® Practitioner, a Rolfer®, a Basic Rolfing Instructor, and recently an Advanced Rolfing Instructor.*

John Schewe: Here we are, I'm one of the editors of *Structure, Function, Integration* and I am talking with Pierpaola Volpones today, an Advanced Training faculty member who lives and practices in Italy. This interview is part of our ongoing series about Advanced Rolfing Instructors and we're going to find out a little bit more about her. Welcome Pierpaola, nice to meet you.

Pierpaola Volpones: Thank you, nice to meet you too.

JS: I'm curious about your background, how many years have you been practicing? What inspired you to become a Rolfer®? What was the process that got you into doing this work?

PV: First I did the Rolf Movement® training, this was in 1985. Then I took my Rolfing Structural Integration (SI) training in 1988. That was a real adventure because the whole thing started when I was working at a swimming pool, teaching kids how to swim, and at some point I was hired to work with a two-year-old baby at the request of her parents. The baby was totally hypotonic and probably there were some autistic traits. The parents expected some improvements of her tonus from the activity in the swimming pool. It was a new experience for me, but I said, "Okay, sure. Why not?"

The child's musculature was totally flaccid, she was unable to sit or stand.

I went to a friend who was in the manual therapy field and told this story, I wanted to know what was possible by touching people; even though the baby was not able to sit or stand, with the tactile stimulation she started to show a desire for a relationship.

I was embracing her, holding her in my arms, and then moving her legs and arms, using the water-resistance to move her in a very *freestyle* way. There was a lot of body contact. After about seven meetings, she started to play with the water with her hands, searching for eye contact, showing some interest for the outside world. I was shocked and said, "Well, what's happening here? Because I'm just hugging her and liking her and loving her, not more than that, but I'm touching her a lot."

I went to a friend who was in the manual therapy field and told this story, I wanted to know what was possible by touching people; even though the baby was not able to sit or stand, with the tactile stimulation she started to show a desire for a relationship. My friend started naming a number of different techniques. Then he said, "I'm organizing a Rolf Movement workshop up here in my office." I said, "What's that?" And he said, "Well, I don't really know what it is but I met the teacher and I liked her a lot, she proposed to organize a workshop and I said yes, here we go." I said, "Okay, fine." So, I trusted him and signed up for the workshop.

The teacher was Leonor Varela (wife of neuroscientist Francisco Varela) and that was in Italy, in Rimini, in my hometown. It was a five-day Rolf Movement workshop, open to anybody. The effects of the work were astonishing to me, for example, even though it was winter and cold, I was sweating a lot. I can say now that I felt a lot of energy mobilized by those tiny, little movements, and awakened awareness. She also had a very new way for me, to encourage us to work with each other, it was a way that I had never experienced before. There was gentleness, respect, and openness. There was a completely different mindset for everything. I was impressed. That was really the first time I was in such an atmosphere that allowed

a new profound contact with my own system, my own body.

JS: So you first experienced Rolf Movement, no touch? There was no hands-on?

PV: Yes. There was no manipulation, no 'Rolfing touch', it was a workshop with embodiment exercises alone, in pairs, and as a group.

Varela said to me, "Pierpaola, you should do this work." And I said, "Well, I don't know what you are talking about, I have no idea about anything." That was in 1984, there was no internet, there was nothing commonly known about Rolfing SI; but I managed to get the Ten Series from Luigi Negro, one of the first Italian Rolfers. I borrowed his Ida Rolf, PhD, books and I could not wait to enter the Rolf Movement training.

It was through the movement workshop, which I first discovered after my swim-instruction work with the baby, that I became interested in what touch and movement can do.

JS: That was the spark.

PV: Yes, that was the spark.

JS: What is your educational background?

PV: I studied physical education, and so, I taught gymnastics in school. Then, I did a university degree in sociology, I taught in school for about ten years. The first degree was three years and the second one was a four-year program.

JS: Okay, so you had seven years of university. Tell us more about your first Rolfer?

PV: Right. My Rolfer was Luigi Negro, like I mentioned, he's from Torino. That was an experience. Really, I was so naïve about everything. There was a funny idea that happened, when he was giving me the sessions, I was visualizing a little skeleton, so tiny. Then the more sessions I had, the skeleton was getting bigger,

a kind of coming into my own system where it was merging into me. It sounds a little bit weird, but this is really what was happening. Definitely it was a way to make peace with my body, it was my way to become comfortable in my flesh.

JS: It's interesting, just as a sideline, I always felt like there was more of 'me' than my body could hold, like I was stuffed in here and it was cramped. After my Ten Series, it was like, "Oh, I fit now," very different.

PV: Yes, totally, I understand what you are saying.

JS: In a broader sense, how has Rolfing SI affected your own body/mind?

PV: The key of it is that I cannot be different from what I do, what I say, or what I teach. Since I'm teaching lines and center and balance, somehow, I have to be there as well. I don't mean I have to be perfect, but I'm aiming for the same thing that I advise. I cannot be totally crooked and then talk about aligned structure. Rolfing SI for me was a way to give me structure, to find coherence in my physical body, in my emotional body, in my thoughts, and in my mindset. It gives me structures like a frame I can juggle within. At the same time, there was a direction, a perspective of where to go, and I could always come back to 'the Line'.

JS: Did you have any physical issues, or structural issues, when you started to notice these changes? Or was your body actually working pretty well?

PV: I had no physical issues, but through the sessions, I discovered some limitations, restrictions, like some back pain when I was standing in a long line up for example. I never paid too much attention to the small signals my body was sending. But I never had big issues. I had a broken clavicle due to a motorbike accident when I was seventeen and had to undergo a surgery. I did recover fast from that injury. When I received my Rolfing sessions, it had been fifteen years since the clavicle injury, and he was working around my clavicle – all that pain came back.

JS: What inspired you to start teaching?

PV: That was also something interesting. As I said, I did my Rolfing training in 1988 and in 1989 Nicholas French was teaching a Basic Rolfing training in Munich and he phoned me asking me to be his assistant. I said, "What? I mean, I've been a Rolfer for one year, why me?" It was because my Rolf Movement instructors had been Janie French (his wife) and Annie Duggan. Janie recommended me because of my movement background, and she had a good opinion of me, I believe. I said, "Well, if you think I can be useful, sure. Why not?" So that was the first time I assisted.

JS: That's pretty rare to assist that soon out of training.

PV: Absolutely.

JS: That's good though, how did it go?

PV: It went very well. Actually, because the class had an uneven number, I was paired up with one of the students. It was a practitioner phase; I think we still had auditing and practitioning phases back then. So I was kind of a senior student in that class as I assisted. Then nothing happened for about ten years. Then Harvey Burns asked me to assist in a Phase I. And Robert Schleip, PhD, also asked me to assist.

In that assisting, I learned a lot. When I was giving my demonstrations, the students were asking, "Why do you do this, or that?" I had to say why I chose my manual and movement interventions so they could learn. I had to verbalize what my hands were spontaneously doing. I had to come into a different mindset to be able to explain while doing. This experience was feeding my work at home. When I was in my office, I was imagining how to answer a question if a student

was watching me working. Through this exercise of searching for the 'why', I was discovering the deepest meaning of Rolfing SI, investigating between the folds of the practice. The result was that my practice took a big leap. I got inspired to continue in that direction.

Harvey said, "Pierpaola, you have to find a motivation for teaching. You have to find an inspiration of why you want to be a teacher." I stayed with this question for some time, kept assisting, until I found it. I'm passionate about the work. I have to say, I love the work. I think we can do good things for people, so I love the idea of being able to transfer this knowledge and these skills. At the same time, I want the students to understand, to develop confidence, to feel safe and secure about the work. It's all right to stay as long as it is needed and balance it, for example.

JS: And when did you become a Basic Rolfing Instructor?

PV: I did my first solo class in 2005.

JS: And how long have you been an Advanced Instructor now?

PV: Right now, just this past year, 2021.

JS: Just recently, okay, congratulations. So you had Luigi Negro, Harvey Burns, Janie French, and Nicholas French. Anyone else that was a big influence in your teaching career?

PV: Pedro Prado, PhD, and Ray McCall. From Pedro I understood the importance of establishing clear relationships, the cleaning up of all the class settings, and making things clear. I had to be clear with myself and listen to the students; knowing where I am at many levels: physical, emotional, and mental. Working with Pedro was impressive, transforming.

JS: Yes. Okay, anyone else? Did you do much work with Peter Schwind?

PV: I did assist Peter in an Advanced Training in 2008, he is a genius and he's a challenge. I think I have learned a lot from

him, in terms of manual approach and body reading. His vision, his point of view, what he brought to the community with all the visceral and membrane work changed our approach in Rolfing SI. Sometimes it is impossible for me to mimic what he does. He has a certain body that I don't have, and he has a certain strength that I don't have. But it's the vision and the details to pay attention to, that make a difference in the work and in the results. So I did not try to be him, but tried to see things from his perspective. Peter was also my supervisor in the Advanced Training teacher training.

JS: What are the challenges between teaching Basic Training and the Advanced Training? What have you noticed; do you have to do a whole different mindset between the two?

PV: Yes, first of all, I have to say, I have only taught one advanced class. I have assisted four times. So I need more teaching practice of the Advanced Training to be able to meet the students' needs. One thing that has come from this process is to recognize what belongs to the Basic Training and what parts can be done afterward, completed during the Advanced Training; in my opinion, Rolfers need to get familiar with the ten-session series, and with a variety of clients and a variety of structures. The Ten Series gives a solid frame to learn and master all the ingredients necessary to understand and practice Rolfing SI for the clients that come to us. With the Advanced Training, we experiment with how to design a series of sessions that respect the principles of Rolfing SI, but that don't have a pre-established protocol to follow. In the Advanced Training we have the client in the foreground. In my opinion, we can work creatively when we have a solid foundation. And there might be a lot of creativity in the advanced work.

JS: Right, well I think that's why they always say they want a minimum of four years of practice before going into the

The key of it is that I cannot be different from what I do, what I say, or what I teach. Since I'm teaching lines and center and balance, somehow, I have to be there as well. I don't mean I have to be perfect, but I'm aiming for the same thing that I advise.

I've listened to Ida teaching on some recordings, I remember one about the adductors, session four, and I remember hearing her talking with the students. This made me so happy, at least I could hear her voice and this helped me to give her a form.

Advanced Training. Because there would be students that would want to go right away and do the Advanced Training. I don't think that would serve them.

PV: No. It really takes time, repetition. And trying the same thing with different people. To build a library in our hands and a way to look at people, a way to relate to them. There are not two back pain cases that are the same, and we cannot successfully treat everyone in the same way.

JS: Right.

PV: When you do something with one person, you try to do the same with the next client that has the same issues. Maybe with the second client, you do the same thing but it doesn't work. By practicing and by trying, we learn, we acquaint ourselves with the reality of our clients through our work. In the beginning of my teaching career I had the tendency to give students as many tools as possible so that they could be successful as Rolfers. Maybe I was tending to give too much, you know?

JS: Right, I think a lot of teachers do that. You get excited. Then when people get overwhelmed, it's hard for them to absorb anything.

PV: And for some people, it's easy to feel lost. When they hear, "You have to be able to work on the kidneys to address back pain," it's for sure something to consider, but for beginners it might be overwhelming and confusing if they are not yet confident in knowing and feeling the layers while they're working.

So I need to be clear, to distinguish what is essential at the beginning. What belongs to the Basic Training, to create the foundation.

JS: How closely do you feel linked to the teachings of Dr. Rolf? Has this changed

over the years? You're like me, a faculty member who never met her. She was already gone by the time we got involved. I was trained in 1987, we're right in the same timeframe. So we are curious about your whole relationship with Dr. Rolf and her teachings, how has that progressed over the years?

PV: Right, somehow I feel I belong to her strength. Michael Salveson was one of my Basic Training teachers and also one of my Advanced Training teachers, he talked a lot about Ida – he calls her Ida. So I always felt close to her through my teachers, she is very present in my sense of the work. Rolfing SI belongs to her. I've listened to Ida teaching on some recordings, I remember one about the adductors, session four, and I remember hearing her talking with the students. This made me so happy, at least I could hear her voice and this helped me to give her a form.

JS: Right, to have those recordings brings us closer to her.

PV: It feels as if I was part of the class, even if I was not in the audience. Also, I watched some of the old videos. There was one video that touched me a lot, she was working with a guy and she was kneeling. The guy was a young man and she was working in the trapezius with her soft fist. Watching her hands and how she was using her body and her voice, it felt like a gift to me, to us.

At some point, in the video where she says, "Okay, I'm working on your trapezius, and now turn your head on the opposite side," she was asking the guy for a movement. That was obviously painful, he was making funny faces. She was saying, "I know it hurts," or something like that, with her fist in the trapezius. Rolfing SI is still sometimes known to be painful and rude, but

watching Ida Rolf, keeping focused on her fist, we need to remember the "keep going" message she was giving as well.

These videos make a bridge with her teaching, I never met her, but I feel grateful.

JS: Oh yes, Rolfing SI changed my life completely. It's interesting how I never thought when I was younger I would be a Rolfer, I didn't even know what a Rolfer was, and here, thirty-three years later, it's the best thing I ever did. Would you say you have your own kind of unique style of Rolfing work? Because I'm pretty sure we all get the same Basic Training, but I know that we all come in with our own ideas, backgrounds, bodies, and everything. When I teach the anatomy classes, I tell them they are going to learn the basics and then they are going to make it their own once they get out and start practicing for a number of years. What is your uniqueness in your work?

PV: I have a preference for the manual approach, for putting my hands on, using my hands to feel, sense, and test. I combine my hands together with my vision. Even though I came from the movement work, I did the movement training before the manual training, yet my first impulse is to touch, to look for physical restrictions, to feel them with my hands. It's my way of connecting with the person. Then, when I'm there, a question comes, for example, "How does it feel?" And, "What would happen if . . . ?" This helps to modulate my touch and refine the connection with the person. I have trained in Somatic Experiencing® (SE), and sometimes I also do SE sessions, differentiated from the Rolfing SI ones. What SE has given me is a more refined capacity to resonate with the client, this is a quality that I bring into my Rolfing sessions. My Rolfing practice benefits from SE, but I don't really mix SE and Rolfing SI. You know what I mean?

JS: Oh yes, I do, that is similar to my relationship with craniosacral work. I don't consider myself a craniosacral therapist but I've got a handful of techniques that I do really well. For me, that's a big integration part at the end, just to finish up. I know we all learned the pelvic lift, but I do a little bit extra at the end, in the last five minutes, just to help their nervous system settle down and integrate.

PV: Listening to you makes me think that what I'm adding in my sessions, partially, it's also the visual intervention. To have a sense of the three-dimensional view of the body, to bring that together with being in relationship with my client, to me this is important. Being in relationship with my client so they are not receiving passively but working together with me.

JS: Can you tell me a little bit more about your thoughts on the whole integration process?

PV: Yes, I think I was assisting Ray McCall when he came to Europe to teach, and he was asking this question to the students, "What is integration?" There was a big pause . . . I proposed the idea that the contralateral movement in walking is a sign of integration. Contralateral movement happens when we move in the three planes, when we have a clear organization of our body structure and capacity to orient in the three planes. To have that, we have to have freedom in our physical body, in the joints, the articular system, so that everything comes together in one phenomenon that we call contralateral movement. It's at the level of limbs and of the spine.

Integration is also when all those different bodies – the physical body, the mental body, and the emotional body – start to be coherent and synchronized together. When they are coherent with one another, they really behave in a way that is fitting to each other, they mirror each other and help each other. Integration is all the different bodies supporting each other somehow.

JS: Very nice, yes, this is a good description. When is your next advanced class, is there one scheduled yet?

PV: Yes, it's scheduled for 2023, in Munich hopefully. I have also been invited to teach in Brazil in 2023.

JS: Right. Most of your classes have been in Munich, correct?

PV: Yes. Munich is our European base. I also taught Basic Training classes in London, and in Italy. I taught my solo advanced class in Italy because there were some Italian Rolfers ready for the Advanced Training. It was a tiny class and we were in the countryside with a beautiful garden, nourished by nature! I will teach a Phase II of Basic Training in Munich this year, April/May 2022, and another one the following year. I've probably taught twenty Basic Trainings since 2005. I am also a Rolf Movement instructor and taught these trainings too.

JS: Nice, so you're a seasoned hand at that now. One last question, are there any changes you think you would want to make in the teaching process?

PV: Probably add more assisted sessions with clients; in Europe, one year after the training is over, Rolfers come back for a supervision class. They practice in their hometowns and then they come back with questions and with experience, looking for refinement and clarifications. I think I would like to have more of that. Having the possibility to work and then revisit and refine together, to have something like an apprenticeship, you know?

JS: Yes, how interesting. The new Rolfers are required to do this? How long does that last?

PV: Yes, it is a six-day class. To have the opportunity to bring some of the difficulties or the issues, even the successes, into a class situation, I think it's a good way to improve their practice. New Rolfers get this big amount of information in one go with Phase II and Phase III, and then they are out in the world on their own.

JS: Yes, that would be good. We don't have that here in North America. There are mentorship situations that people can set up on their own, but there's no specific course other than coming back and doing continuing education workshops, those three-day, four-day, and six-day workshops. Other than that, you're taking it on yourself. I was fortunate, I had a Rolfer in New Orleans who had been working for a couple of years and we worked on each other, I was constantly peppering him with questions when he was working on me and I was working with him.

PV: Yes, exactly.

JS: Well, I think that is all our questions, you are very well spoken, Pierpaola, thank you for meeting with me today.

PV: Thank you for the interview, I feel like I'm seen and heard.

JS: Well, the community has grown since we got into it, it is really nice to see how much Rolfing SI and Rolf Movement Integration has grown and continued on. Good luck with all your work and teaching in the future.

Pierpaola Volpones discovered Rolfing SI through bodywork and her research into well-being and somatic expression. She studied in Munich with Stacey Mills and Michael Salveson in her Basic Training and with Michael Salveson and Jeffrey Maitland in her Advanced Training. Her Rolf Movement training took place in Italy with Janie French and Annie Duggan. She began her Rolfing SI and Rolf Movement teacher training almost twenty years ago, and she has been teaching since 2005. She runs a practice in Rimini, Italy, and teaches for the European Rolfing® Association. Her website is www.volpones.it.

John Schewe completed his Basic Training in 1987 and his Advanced Training in 1991. He has been a member of the Life Sciences Group at the Dr. Ida Rolf Institute® since 2007 and has taught numerous anatomy lead-in classes. Though his academic background is in geology (MS, Louisiana State University, 1979), John has had a keen interest in the biological sciences as they pertain to bodywork in general and Rolfing SI in particular.

He lives in Athens, Georgia with his wife, Laura, and maintains a practice there.

Cultural Humility in the Therapeutic Relationship

By Anne Hoff, Certified Advanced Rolfer®

Anne Hoff

ABSTRACT *Rolfing® Structural Integration attracts a broad range of clients from diverse backgrounds. Part of our job as Rolfers® is to create a positive therapeutic relationship with each client as the container for effective, transformative work. 'Cultural humility' is a commitment to be with our clients in a way that welcomes and values their unique identities.*

Introduction

This article is an addition to the discussion of diversity/inclusivity begun in recent issues of *Structure, Function, Integration: The Journal of the Dr. Ida Rolf Institute®*. I was introduced to the concepts of cultural humility, location of self, and broaching through a graduate program in counseling with Saybrook University. I profess no expertise in these areas. I often feel awkwardness, and sometimes identify uncomfortable blind spots, yet I find the self-awareness that results always leads to growth and greater sensitivity to my clients. I share this material in the hope it will support others.

I first learned about the concept of *cultural humility* when assigned the article "Cultural Humility: A Therapeutic Framework for Engaging Diverse Clients" (Mosher et al. 2017), written for a therapy journal. However, the term was coined

by Melanie Tervalon, MD, MPH, and Jann Murray-García, MD, MPH (1998), in response to a growing call for physicians to be responsive to clients of differing cultural, racial, and ethnic backgrounds. The concept of *cultural humility* arises from discussions of how practitioners of varying social memberships can meet an increasingly diverse client population with sensitivity and respect, whether for their race, culture, sexual orientation, or any other aspect of their identity.

Cultural humility supplants an earlier emphasis on *cultural competence* (Mosher et al. 2017). Cultural competence was an attempt to meet multiculturalism through gaining the skills and knowledge to have a competency particularly when service providers who belong to the majority social group are working with people who belong to a minority group. The cultural-competence model puts the onus on practitioners to educate

The concept of *cultural humility* arises from discussions of how practitioners of varying social memberships can meet an increasingly diverse client population with sensitivity and respect, whether for their race, culture, sexual orientation, or any other aspect of their identity.

themselves on the many types of cultures they could encounter. Time exposed the fallacies inherent in that idea: first, how could one ever have a complete working knowledge of the multiplicity of cultures, etc., our world presents? Second, while individuals may be members of a particular group (e.g., African-American), they are still individuals who have a multiplicity of intersecting identities (e.g., gender, sexual identity, religion), so generalizations around group identity may or may not apply.

In contrast, rather than focusing on a knowledge base to be acquired, cultural humility implies "a commitment and active engagement in a lifelong process that individuals enter into on an ongoing basis with patients, communities, colleagues, and with themselves" (L. Brown 1994, quoted in Tervalon and Murray-García 1998). It is based on "ways of *being with clients* that prioritize and value diverse cultural identities" (Mosher et al. 2017, 222). It invites us to step into relationship, inviting forward all of the client's identities and showing up with an awareness of our own.

Hypothetical Clients

This article will posit some hypothetical clients of diverse identities as a way to discuss cultural humility and introduce the approaches of *location of self* and *broaching* as ways to support the therapeutic relationship. In creating these fictitious clients, I've considered times in my practice over the years where I have felt an uncertainty of how to engage based on our differences and my lack of knowledge. These scenarios all assume that we are meeting at my office for a first session without any prior orientation.

Client 1: I look at my schedule and see the name of a new client. I don't know how to pronounce the first name, Urwa, and I don't know what gender it's associated with. I know nothing from the notes provided with

the booking except that the client is coming in for low back pain and found me on Yelp. Shortly before the appointment time, two people are outside my home office – a woman in a hijab, and a man; perhaps they are a couple? Which one is my client? How do I initiate contact?

Client 2: The client booking is under the name Karl. There's a note saying they use they/them as pronouns and are coming to start a Ten Series. My booking system requires pre-payment for the first session, and the credit card has the same last name as Karl, but the first name of Katherine. Karl arrives, a young person in their twenties with what I consider a fairly androgynous look. We do the usual conversation around their presenting issues and body history. Then I say we'll do a body reading, with them in underwear if comfortable. They disrobe to a layer of men's underwear and a tank top.

Client 3: My new client Terrence is an African-American man in his early thirties who recently moved from Minneapolis to Seattle to start a job at Amazon. Terrence tells me he injured his neck in a car accident some years ago, and has had terrible migraines since then. He's seen doctors, chiropractors, massage therapists, acupuncturists, you name it . . . Nothing has helped much. A coworker suggested he try Rolfing® Structural Integration (SI).

Identity Questions

An important piece of cultural humility is understanding one's key identities, as we are interacting from those whether we realize it or not. In my case, I'm a White woman, sixty-one years old, and I consider myself heterosexual, politically liberal, and spiritual but not religious. I've lived in a number of places – Wisconsin,

Tokyo, Maui, Seattle – and each has shaped me. I've long considered myself a feminist and LGBTQ+ ally.

Despite considering myself quite open, in each of the fictitious client outlines above, I'd have a certain awkwardness, arising from differences in culture or social location. Let's consider some of the aspects of each scenario. I have a great curiosity about people, and always like to ask questions and learn about people's backgrounds, yet questions need to be asked with sensitivity, or sometimes invited rather than asked. A question as simple as "Where are you from?" can be felt as a microaggression if someone feels you are asking it from a prejudicial consideration.

With my first client, I learn that Urwa is the female and that she is with her husband. Would they take offense if I ask where they are from, or would they welcome my interest? From the hijab, I assume Urwa is Muslim. It seems her husband is planning to be there with us in the room for the duration of the session. Usually, I would find that annoying and ask the partner not receiving the session to go get a coffee and come back when the session is ending. But I remember that a male Muslim friend once told me that he should only receive bodywork from a female with his wife present. Is there a cultural norm here as well? Do I ask?

With Karl, while I was greeting them, I become aware of the binary idea of gender I was acculturated to in my upbringing, and that was also the default thinking during my Rolfing training, as we didn't discuss gender outside the binary. We're doing the first first session of the Ten Series, about opening breath, so ideally I'd like hand-to-skin access along the rib cage. For a cis-gender man, I usually ask that he remove his shirt; for a cis-gender woman, I usually ask her to disrobe to bra or sports bra, or fold up her shirt. I know from Karl's pronouns that they most likely don't identify as

The practitioner initiates the conversation, which signals that there is openness to dialogue about identities and how they affect both the therapeutic relationship and life outside of the Rolfing context.

binary male or female, and the tank top may be signaling a boundary. I find myself wondering if Karl is transgender. Katherine could be another person who paid for the session, or Katherine may be Karl's government name that they have not legally changed. Maybe Karl has had a top surgery, which could indicate fascial or scar-tissue issues relevant to our first-session work. I'm curious, and I don't want to be intrusive.

With Terrence, I am very aware that I am a White woman. Despite living in various regions of the United States and overseas, I've never lived anywhere with a large African-American population. I grew up near Minneapolis, where Terrence moved from, and I am well aware that there is often prejudice there too, despite the larger African-American population. How was Terrence affected by the murder of George Floyd? How will he feel with my White hands on his neck, even in a therapeutic context? Would he rather be working with a Rolfer who is BIPOC (Black, Indigenous, Person of Color)? I wonder about the power dynamics inherent in the Rolfing SI relationship: similar to the way a male Rolfer has to consider the impact of his gender when doing sessions with female clients, what do I need to consider about being White as I do a session with an African-American person? I want to help Terrence with his physical issue, and I know from experience that Rolfing SI will sometimes help when nothing else has, but is any cultural conversation about our differences needed to create ease?

Location of Self

One suggested approach to cultural humility is a model from mental-health therapy called *location of self* where the practitioner "self-discloses his or her social locations and invites a conversation about how the intersection of the identities held by the [practitioner and client] may be beneficial and/or limiting" (Watts-Jones 2010, 405). The idea is pretty elementary. The practitioner initiates the

conversation, which signals that there is openness to dialogue about identities and how they affect both the therapeutic relationship and life outside of the Rolfing context. If I initiate this conversation with comfort, it tells the client that their identities are welcome and dialogue is welcome. Watts-Jones (2010) notes both risks and benefits to the location of self, as well as the consideration that needs to be given to what and how to self-disclose.

Watts-Jones notes three assumptions that underlie the location of self. These are from her context as a family therapist, but I think there are grounds for considering the interplay in our work as well.

- First, *the practitioner needs a certain comfort with themself to have these conversations in a way that generates safety for the client*. In the posture of cultural humility, the practitioner works to develop a comfort with their own identities and with welcoming the client's identities as the basis for the location-of-self dialogue being constructive.

- Second, Watts-Jones notes that identities matter and are present in the therapeutic relationship, especially identities related to social status and power. The issue here is particularly around blind spots based on how we view the world through our identities, especially if we belong to the majority group. In the November issue of this journal, Pheonix DeLeón (2021) shared the ADDRESSING model, which highlights many types of cultural memberships and invites a practitioner to consider their own identities and those of their client, and whether each is in the dominant or non-dominant societal group. In the July issue, Katy Loeb (2021) explored how economics limits access to Rolfing work. She notes that "In a capitalist system, which monetizes our bodily experiences and labor, our prices represent how we value ourselves and Rolfing

Structural Integration"; the result is Rolfers "charge rates that entire communities cannot possibly afford" (Loeb 2021, 67). When I think about my clients over the years, I remember some who had low-pay jobs and my uncomfortable awareness of just how much hourly labor they had to do to pay for each session.

- The third assumption Watts-Jones highlights is that we are all influenced by oppression as it is deeply ingrained in the dominant culture's ways of thinking, its value system, its institutions, and its cultural practices. She suggests we, therefore, consider for each client how oppression shows up, even when it is not obvious or clear in the history: "seeing the legacy of wounds and entitlements that run underground as well as those that surface in relationships, and [providing] a space for witnessing and healing these" (Watts-Jones 2010, 411). Moreover, oppression is also molded into our bodies: I refer readers in particular to the work of Resmaa Menakem (2017) on cultural somatics and embodied historical trauma, and to the various articles included in the diversity and inclusion themes in the July 2021 and November 2021 issues of this journal.

The Location of Self Dialogue

Moving from the theoretical to the practical, what might a location-of-self dialogue look like with a Rolfing client? This is something I'm just slowly moving into myself, having been introduced to this only a few months back, so I'm feeling my way forward. Perhaps I'd start with my usual descriptions of Rolfing work and taking the client's history, but before moving into the body reading and table work, I'd make some general remarks along these lines [drawing on an example Watts-Jones (2010) gives]:

Before going further, I'd like to share a bit about myself. Our work together is based on my training in Rolfing SI, but I'm also here as a person with all of my background and experiences that give me a lens to view the world and that also can cause blind spots. So I'd like to consider how my personal identities might be either helpful or a limitation in our work together and get your thoughts about this. And this is something we can talk about at any point in the work that either of us feels we are perhaps encountering a bump in the road.

Then, as I imagine my hypothetical clients, it would go a bit differently for each.

With Urwa and her husband, I would want to share something like this:

I'm an American woman, and while I have traveled and am curious about other cultures and religions, there are many I don't have much familiarity with. I want to approach everyone's culture and religion with respect, so I invite you to tell me about any customs and beliefs that are important to you as we work together in a setting like this, where you will be touched as part of the sessions. In Rolfing sessions, we often look at the body with outer clothing removed, so we can see muscles and body alignment more clearly, but we don't have to do this if it is not appropriate to you or your culture. Similarly, I usually work with just my client present, but I'm happy to have your husband here if that is what is most comfortable for you.

With Karl, I might say this:

To help you understand the lenses of my life experience, Karl, I'd like to share that I'm in my sixties, so I'm from a different generation than you. I identify as a straight woman, and also as a feminist and an LGBTQ+ ally. I believe in honoring each person's gender identity and want to be cognizant of any gender-related issues, emotional or physical, that may impact our work together. I appreciate you sharing with me the pronouns you use,

and I invite you to share anything else about your identities that feels important to you and to our work together.

With Terrence, I would consider saying something like this.

I'm a White woman in my sixties. I grew up in the Midwest, not far from Minneapolis, so while we have differences I also know a bit of the city you last lived in. I invite you to let me know any of your identities that feel important to share.

Then, after Terrence's response, I could go on and say:

There is a lot of awareness right now about racial trauma and how trauma is held in the body. I wonder if there is anything relevant to you that I might need to be aware of based on our racial identities? I invite this to be an ongoing dialogue as we work, particularly if I do or say anything that makes you feel uncomfortable.

Beyond the Initial Interview

There can be other times besides the initial client interview that it is important to broach gender, ethnic, racial, or other identities.

For example, it would be useful for a male practitioner working with a female client who has disclosed a trauma history that includes sexual abuse by a male relative to broach these issues at various junctures. A discussion might be appropriate in advance of a Fourth Hour, so she would be aware ahead of time of the areas that would be worked and could consider how she wanted to dress (perhaps sports shorts instead of underwear) or if/how she wanted to be draped. And any time the Rolfer saw a nervous-system response that suggested activation, he might want to at the least slow down or pause, but also consider circling back to the earlier conversation and explicitly stating, "I'm wanting to see how you are doing. It's important to me

that you feel in control of the work. I'm aware of the history you told me about, and I'm wondering if you'd like a pause in my hands-on work for you to check in to anything that is arising?" You'll see that this is not particularly different than what a good Rolfer would be doing anyway; fortunately, Rolfing trainings have often considered the power dynamic of the therapeutic relationship, particularly as it pertains to male practitioners and female clients. Plus, thanks especially to the work of Peter Levine, PhD, in developing Somatic Experiencing®, our community has a fairly sophisticated understanding of trauma.

We should also be aware of the news and how our clients might be impacted. If we have a client who has shared a Jewish identity, we might speak to that if they come in after there is news of a synagogue attack, even if it's not local. Has it affected them and their sense of safety? Does it affect the therapeutic relationship and the vulnerability inherent in being a client receiving our work? Similarly, if we have an African-American client on the day there's been a significant judicial verdict, one that either brings justice or one that alternatively causes pain, it can be important to check-in with how the client is doing, and note any identities at play in the therapeutic relationship. To not speak to something that may be a pressing concern for the client can reduce the sense of safety in the therapeutic relationship.

Conclusion

We each go through life shaped by our life experiences and identifying ourselves based on memberships in various cultural, religious, ethnic, or other groups. We see in our society the division and suffering caused by the failure to give value to the experiences and identities of people with non-dominant identities. If our work is to be truly therapeutic, it

We see in our society the division and suffering caused by the failure to give value to the experiences and identities of people with non-dominant identities. If our work is to be truly therapeutic, it must welcome the whole person in all of their identities and make space for them.

must welcome the whole person in all of their identities and make space for them. This is supported by a stance of cultural humility – an openness and regard for others and diversity – and location of self as a particular approach to building a safe and open therapeutic container.

Writing this article has been part of my own ongoing journey with cultural humility. I learned about this concept in a didactic setting, and I see layers of vulnerability and timidity come forward as I contemplate the important work of bringing it into my professional life. It's supportive to remember that this is a lifelong process; it's about developing a way of being, rather than a polished skillset.

Anne Hoff is a Certified Advanced Rolfer in Seattle, Washington. For many years she was involved in the editing and management of this Journal.

References

DeLéon, P. L. Q. 2021. Working across difference in structural integration. *Structure, Function, Integration: The Journal of the Dr. Ida Rolf Institute*® 49(3):58-64.

Loeb, K. 2021. Reimagining equitable economics in Rolfing® SI. *Structure, Function, Integration: The Journal of the Dr. Ida Rolf Institute*® 49(2):67-69.

Menakem, Resmaa. 2017. *My grandmother's hands: Racialized trauma and the pathway to mending our hearts and bodies.* Las Vegas, NV:Central Recovery Press.

Mosher, D. K., J. Hook, L. Captari, and D. Davis 2017. Cultural humility: A therapeutic framework for engaging diverse clients. *Practice Innovations* 2(4):221-233. doi:10.1037/pri0000055

Tervalon, M., and J. Murray-García, J. 1998. Cultural humility versus cultural competence: A critical distinction in defining physician training outcomes in multicultural education. *Journal of Health Care for the Poor and Underserved, 9,* 117–125. http:// dx.doi.org/10.1353/ hpu.2010.0233

Watts-Jones, T. D. 2010 September. Location of self: Opening the door to dialogue on intersectionality in the therapy process. *Family Process 49(3):405-420.*

Review

Books edited by the
European Guild for Structural
Integration, Robert Schleip
and Jan Wilke

***Structural Integration – The Basic Series
in All Its Abundance, An Homage to Dr.
Ida Rolf's Work Inspired* by John Lodge**
by European Guild for Structural Integration
(Published by the European Guild for
Structural Integration Ltd. 2021)

Reviewed by Allan Kaplan, Certified Advanced Rolfer®

When I was approached to review "the John Lodge book," I was intrigued: I'd known John – not well, but we had the occasional chat. I looked forward to learning more of this giant of our community, 'giant' because he was a formidable fellow: I met him at one of my first regional Rolfing® meetings in the late 1980s, and I remember him as somewhat over six feet with a massive presence, my strongest memory being his booming voice in response to something I'd said, " . . . the root fascia! – affect the root fascia!" Okay, I'd work toward that!

When the book arrived, I was instantly struck by the care and craftsmanship that had been invested in the volume, and I say 'volume', because it's no cheap paperback – within its cloth covers are pages of thick, crisp paper; sharp, clean photos and reproductions; and a ribbon to hold my place. It's clear that Aleš Urbanczik and the European Guild for Structural Integration took their mission seriously, and it really was a grand undertaking. At first blush, the reading of it was a little bit of a challenge, trying to place how all the parts fit together – not exactly a biography of either Dr. Rolf or Lodge, not an analysis of structural integration, not a how-to, not just a compendium of testimonials of the work. But as I continued on, it became obvious how all these pieces had been melded together into, as promised, a tribute not just to Ida P. Rolf, PhD, her life's work, and her seminal book, *Rolfing: The Integration of Human Structures* (1977), but to the culmination and heart of her efforts, what we have come to know as the Ten Series, or the 'Recipe', as seen through the archives of her book's artist, John Lodge.

John was a tremendous artist, and I clearly remember going to his house, being struck by the number of large, varied canvases on his walls, and learning that he had painted them all. Dr. Rolf had been impressed with his talents, too, and utilized him to work with her book, helping with the text and providing the illustrations. Through a fortuitous chain of events, Urbanczik was gifted Lodge's notes, book drafts, and artifacts, and through them, we find insights into the development of the founder of Rolfing Structural Integration (SI) and her art. In addition to a presentation of the concepts and thinking of Dr. Rolf, we are treated to excellent reproductions of original draft pages of her manuscript with notes in her hand, along with Lodge's own editorial records.

It is clear that Lodge dedicated himself to aiding Dr. Rolf in her goal to spread and preserve her thoughts, her theories, her tenets, obeying her directions in drafting exacting drawings, and helping edit her drafts. But what is also evident is the impact the guru had on the student, and the devotion he expressed in carrying out his tasks. After her book was published and she had left us, John still strived to carry on her teachings. We find original notes he made for himself, and ultimately for the classes he taught at the then Rolf Institute® (now known as the Dr. Ida Rolf Institute®) – notes on the Recipe and esoterica from those formative years of Rolfing SI. For me, seeing them brought back deeply familiar reminiscences from my own long-ago training, reliving those heady days with my teachers, Emmett Hutchins and Peter Melchior; these illustrations were reminders of not only basic Rolfing concepts and ideals, but also of the cryptic amalgamation of lore and mysticism that Dr. Rolf apparently gleaned from her studies in Egypt, yoga, Semantics, and other arcanum that I'd heard quoted in class. As with most notes, the notetaker is typically the only person with the ability to understand them fully, but, hopefully, readers will find them as thought-provoking as I did.

In my later contact with John, after the occasional phone call, I found that time had taken its toll: The giant had grown shorter than me. He had fallen, at one point, as I recall, and his back had become an issue. When I had initially gotten a session from John, I'd quizzed him as to what he'd seen, what his strategy would be, and I found his response atypical; while John took Polaroid photos before a session like many Rolfers, he would then draw lines through the joints with a ruler, showing deviations from the horizontal, like a number of the book's illustrations, relying on this as his sole assessment process as we headed into our session. "If it was good enough for Dr. Rolf, it's good enough for me. Let's get started" still rings in my ears.

Structural Integration – The Basic Series in All Its Abundance is an important contribution to the legacy of Ida Rolf. As we all age, the original holders of Dr. Rolf's teachings are disappearing, and it is up to the second and third generations of her followers to perpetuate her insights. Aside from the few papers Dr. Rolf published, there are only two books that contain her words and teachings, *Rolfing: The Integration of Human Structures* (1977) [whose second edition was titled *Rolfing: Reestablishing the Natural Alignment and Structural Integration of the Human Body for Vitality and Well-Being* (1989)], and *Ida Rolf Talks About Rolfing and Physical Reality* (1978) [the current printing title for this book is *Rolfing and Physical Reality* (1990). Now, we have a third. *Structural Integration – The Basic Series in All Its Abundance* is unique in that we are presented with a snapshot of Rolfing SI's formative years, when its founder was striving to leave a written legacy. The context for Rolf's project is laid out with the biographical material, photos, crisp document reproductions, a taste of her mysticism, and personal testimonials, some from those who knew her in the day. The volume is an asset for any practitioner that wants deeper insight into the work, and the woman who developed it.

References

Rolf, I. P. 1977. *Rolfing: The integration of human structures.* Santa Monica, CA: Dennis-Landman Publishing.

———.1978. *Ida Rolf talks about Rolfing and physical reality.* (R. Feitis, ed.) Boulder, CO: Rolf Institute.

———. 1989. *Rolfing: Reestablishing the natural alignment and structural integration of the human body for vitality and well-being.* Rochester, VT: Healing Arts Press.

———. 1990. *Rolfing and physical reality.* Rochester, VT: Healing Arts Press.

Fascia in Sport and Movement, Second Edition, Edited by Robert Schleip and Jan Wilke (Handspring Publishing 2021)

Reviewed by Jeffrey Kinnunen, MS, Certified Rolfer®

Ida P. Rolf, PhD, recognized that fascia forms a tensional framework inside the body. Rolf's theory of organizing the human body along the vertical line of gravity and facilitating an unencumbered expression of movement suggests that structural integration engages with the fascia. Consequently, the work of Rolf and her students propelled us towards a better understanding of the role of fascia in the body. The editors of this second edition of *Fascia in Sport and Movement* are modern torchbearers of this legacy. Robert Schleip, PhD, an international Rolfing® instructor and Feldenkrais Method® teacher, is the director of the Fascia Research Project in Ulm, Germany, and the Research Director of the European Rolfing® Association. Jan Wilke, PhD, is a strength and conditioning coach and researcher who leads the 'Fascia in Motion' research group at Frankfurt University, Germany. The individual research, and collaboration between Schleip and Wilke, has evolved the scientific and medical understanding of fascia in the body.

The pair produced the first edition of *Fascia in Sport and Movement* in 2015, providing movement practitioners with recommendations for practical application based on fascia research. The second edition, reviewed here, is more than a mere update to the first edition. Instead, editors Schleip and Wilke with assistant editor Amanda Baker offer an impressive expansion of the first edition. There is so much updated here, that it could almost be viewed as an entirely new book. The second publication is composed of forty-eight chapters with contributions from fifty-three authors, divided into three sections: theory, assessment, and clinical application. The result is a reference that I would highly recommend for anyone who practices or studies manual therapy or movement therapy.

This volume has a visually appealing design and format. I appreciate the use of glossy pages, and find the type easy to read. The images are clean and colorful; complimenting the text effectively. The information presented by Schleip and Wilke, and all the authors, is intended for practitioners, yet is reasonably accessible. The theory and assessment sections were written in an academic manner, based on updated clinical evidence. The final section, clinical application, generally builds on ideas presented in the first two sections. The structure of the book suggests to me that the reader can follow components of the first two sections, with à la carte chapter selection in the final section based on individual relevance. The topics covered in the third section vary considerably. Topics include the implications of our myofascial system in various specific sports and activities, suggestions for how to adapt movement and fitness modalities based on the modern understanding of fascia, and implications that carry over into tissue manipulation and dietary choices. Many topics float outside of my interests, although some of those different perspectives have stimulated me more than the information inside my interests. Ideas are consolidated from disparate sources, and the philosophical connective tissue between a multitude of disciplines becomes evident.

Many of the chapters are incredibly informative, and I gained a deeper understanding of topics that I have already read about extensively. This is natural when so many experts have come in as contributors. Some chapters are truly outstanding, including the offerings from Wilke and Schleip, as well as the chapter on palpatory and functional assessment by the late Leon Chaitow. The multitude of contributors here is mostly a strength, but sometimes falters into a weakness. For example, occasional shifts in the nomenclature occur. Some information in the third section ventures past the evidence and into the realm of speculation (more on that later in the review). Another complaint that I noted is that I did come across some occasional typographical/contextual errors.

Putting those criticisms aside, the narrative as a whole is greater than the sum of the parts. I consistently found clinical pearls that moved me to rethink my own approach. I found myself reading the chapters in a nonlinear fashion, revisiting previous chapters when new ideas grabbed me. For example, the combination of Chapter 44, rehabilitation in sport medicine, and Chapters 13 and 14 covering force transmission through myofascial chains and synergistic/antagonistic muscles, sparked ideas about using my assessment tools to illuminate causes of dysfunction, rather than the symptoms of dysfunction. Additionally, the exploration of fascia as a sensory organ in Chapter 15, and the philosophy of three-dimensional fascia training in Chapter 40 left me to conclude that I could produce similar or better results by spending more time on gentle, indirect techniques.

Some of my favorite chapters covered information that I expected to be irrelevant to me. Chapter 33 discussed overarm throwing, beautifully highlighting how a human being is designed for this primitive motion. The concept immediately altered my perspective on how I should approach shoulder-girdle restrictions. It is difficult not to enthusiastically endorse a product to other Rolfers®, when it both teaches and inspires curiosity.

When I was introduced to fascia in an undergraduate anatomy class in the early 1990s, it was described as a material that holds space in the body. Fascia, as my professor explained, was believed to function like the expanded polystyrene blocks that keep electronics from rattling around in their boxes. More than twenty years later, I had observed repeating patterns of movement restriction in hundreds of my open-heart-surgery patients while working as an exercise physiologist in a hospital-based cardiac rehabilitation program. My desire to understand and treat these phenomena led to my discovery of the prolific fascia research of several authors, including Wilke and Schleip. Fascia is integral to the structure, function, and somatic-sensation in vertebrates. My personal interest in fascia altered my understanding of kinesiology and physiology at that time, acting as a catalyst for my study of Rolfing Structural Integration (SI).

A tricky point for me as a Rolfing SI practitioner is that I have witnessed expert practitioners accomplish a level of change with their clients that seemed impossible. The explanations that have been passed down through the oral tradition of practitioners are often poetic, metaphorical, or based on subjective perceptive experiences. I embrace the value in these explanations, but I have also had to answer client concerns when they have read the Wikipedia page on Rolfing SI, or find it conflated with a number of practices that have been identified as quackery, or based on pseudoscientific principles.

That brings me to the final point that I would like to illustrate as a value in this book. As I stated earlier, some components of the clinical application section drift away from the established evidence. Schleip and Wilke recognize this, and address it in Chapter 23, titled "Integrating clinical experience and evidence: Roadmap for a healthy dialog between health practitioners and academic researchers." When we can communicate effectively with researchers (or in general with practitioners from a multitude of areas), it elevates our place within the larger community. Since we have inherited Rolf's ideas, it behooves us to understand the core science surrounding fascia. Remaining scientifically literate on the subject fosters communication between practitioners in a multitude of areas, and ensures that we can all speak the same language. It also differentiates us from a spectrum of industries for whom fascia has merely become a buzzword. A Google search reveals the burgeoning lists of practitioners promising to "train, fix, treat, manipulate, adjust, release, etc." fascia, seemingly alluding to it as a bad actor in human existence.

My conclusion is that *Fascia in Sport and Movement*, Second Edition by Schleip and Wilke, is a collaboration that rises beyond fads, and continues the influence of a number of pioneers, including the work of Dr. Ida P. Rolf. The information contained here could be found elsewhere, but may also offer value in perspectives that you did not expect. If you see a benefit in understanding the current science surrounding fascia, this will be an authoritative addition to your library.

Institute News

Upcoming USA Classes 2022-2023

2022-2023* Rolfing® SI Basic Training

Boulder, CO Campus

Program	Start Date
P1.22 Basic Training	March 7, 2022
P3.22 Basic Training	June 6, 2022
P4.22 Basic Training	October 3, 2022
P1.23 Basic Training	January 9, 2023
P3.23 Basic Training	June 5, 2023

2022-2023 Rolf Movement® Integration Certification (Intensive)**

Boulder, CO Campus

Course	Start Date
RMI1.22	April 25, 2022
RMI2.22	July 11, 2022
RMI3.22	September 19, 2022
RMI1.23	May 1, 2023
RMI2.23	July 24, 2023
RMI3.23	October 16, 2023

2022 Advanced Training

Boulder, CO Campus

Program	Start Date
AT1.22	Part 1 / September 5, 2022 Part 2 / October 31, 2022

* All classes including continuing education can be found at rolf.org

** The RMI classes listed are for our 30 Day Intensive Program and includes three parts. We also offer a Workshop Format that can be completed over time for added flexibility from various USA locations.

Upcoming Continuing Education Courses

The Dr. Ida Rolf Institute® is committed to cultivating academic growth and therapeutic skills in all of its graduates. Continuing education studies can cover a broad range of relevant subjects. Certified Rolfers® may take workshops in specific manipulative techniques or may explore other related subjects such as craniosacral therapy or visceral manipulation. Classes are continually being added – please visit www.rolf.org/courses for the most recent updates, or to register.

Contacts

**Officers &
Board of Directors**

Libby Eason (Faculty, Chair)
bodfaculty2rep@rolf.org

Paul Van Alstine (Western USA)
bodwesternrep@rolf.org

Florian Thomas (Europe)
bodeuropeanrep@rolf.org

Juan David Velez (Faculty)
bodfaculty1rep@rolf.org

Cosper Scafidi (Eastern USA, Treasurer)
bodeasternrep@rolf.org

Greice Gobbi (International)
bodinternationalrep@rolf.org

Ines Hoffmann (At-Large, Secretary)
bodatlarge2@rolf.org

Jenny Rock (At-Large)
bodatlarge1@rolf.org

Dan Somers (Central & Mountain USA)
bodcentralrep@rolf.org

Executive Board Members

Libby Eason
Ines Hoffman
Cosper Scafidi

Education Executive Committee

Neal Anderson, Chair
Tessy Brungardt
Lisa Fairman
Larry Koliha
Kevin McCoy
Adam Mentzell
Juan David Velez

Dr. Ida Rolf Institute®

5055 Chaparral Ct., Ste. 103
Boulder, CO 80301
+1-303 449-5903

www.rolf.org

info@rolf.org

Dr. Ida Rolf Institute Staff

Christina Howe
Executive Director/Chief Academic Officer

Mary Contreras
Director of Admissions
& Recruitment

Samantha Sherwin
Director of Faculty & Student Services

Shellie Marsh
Office Manager

Brazilian Rolfing Association

Sally Nakai, Administrator
Associação Brasileira de Rolfing - ABR
R. Cel. Arthur de Godoy, 83
Vila Mariana
04018-050-SãoPaulo-SP
Brazil

+55-11-5574-5827
+55-11-5539-8075 fax
www.rolfing.com.br
rolfing@rolfing.com.br

European Rolfing Association e.V.

Sabine Klausner
Saarstrasse 5
80797 Munchen
Germany
+49-89 54 37 09 40
+49-89 54 37 09 42 fax

www.rolfing.org
info@rolfing.org

Japanese Rolfing Association

Yukiko Koakutsu, Foreign Liaison
Omotesando Plaza 5th Floor
5-17-2 Minami Aoyama
Minato-ku Tokyo, 107-0062
Japan
+81+3-6868-3548

www.rolfing.or.jp
jra@rolfing.or.jp

Rolfing® Association of Canada

Hyatt Saikin, Chair
Suite 289, 17008 - 90 Ave
Edmonton, AB T5T 1L6
Canada
+1-416 804-5973
(905) 648-3743 fax

www.rolfingcanada.org
info@rolfingcanada.org

Made in the USA
Middletown, DE
11 January 2023

21390017R00051